MACKINAC BRIDGE

A 50-YEAR CHRONICLE · 1957-2007

BY MIKE FORNES

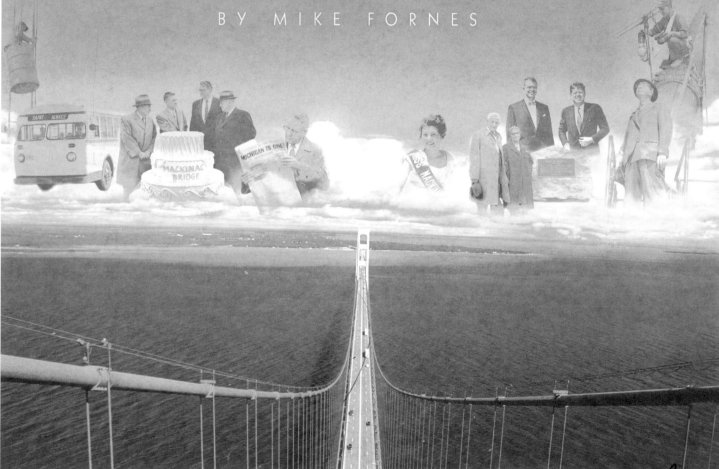

by Mike Fornes

Foreword by Lawrence A. Rubin

Cheboygan Tribune Printing Co.
308 N. Main St.
Cheboygan, Michigan 49721

ISBN 978-1-4243-2930-4

1st Printing — April, 2007

Front & back cover photos courtesy of Michigan Department of Transportation
Cover photo-illustrations by Charles Borowicz and Renee Glass
Layout & page designs by Dan Pavwoski

For additional copies of this book, send $35 (includes tax, postage & handling) to:
Mike Fornes – PO Box 305, Mackinaw City, MI 49701

Table of Contents

Foreword

By
LAWRENCE A. RUBIN
Executive Secretary, Mackinac Bridge Authority 1950-1984

Mike Fornes has completed a monumental task in writing the history of the Mackinac Bridge since it opened 50 years ago.

Let me give you a clue:

The operation, maintenance and repair of the structure are divided into three eight-hour shifts. The key individual during each shift is the operations supervisor. His or her desk is positioned in the Administration Building so that he/she can observe the fare booths, the fare plaza and down the center of the bridge as far as normal vision allows. This view of bridge traffic has been more recently augmented by the installation of video cameras mounted all the way across the bridge deck.

One of the duties of the operations supervisors is to maintain a report of occurrences during their shifts. Simple arithmetic tells us that during the first 50 years of bridge operations there have been some 18,250 reports filed – 50 x 365 x 3. Of course, many of the midnight to dawn shifts were routine.

Nevertheless, Mike had to examine all of them. A formidable task!

In addition, his in-depth investigations of the accidents that occurred on the bridge in the past half-century have been most revealing in that the police reports and newspaper coverage provided far more additional information than the operations reports.

I said in 1985 when writing my own book about the bridge's construction years that it was my intent to report in detail the events from 1950 to 1957 that led to the opening of the Mackinac Bridge. I added that history often depends upon the perch from which the observer reports the battle.

Mike Fornes has picked up the task of reporting 50 years of happenings on the bridge from there and has documented a great story about a magnificent structure.

Lawrence A. Rubin
April, 2007

Dedication

This book is about the Mackinac Bridge.

At the same time, it is a book about people. There are people who crossed the bridge, crossed under it and over it. Nearly all completed their journeys safely, but some did not.

However, the theme that continually rang true while writing this work was that remarkable people have cared for this bridge since it opened in 1957. Without them, the Mackinac Bridge would be like so many other public or government-run facilities – sort of anonymous in the sense that they are not cared for in the same way as the Mighty Mac.

The Mackinac Bridge has a very definite personality; one that changes with the seasons and with the weather. It is different with each sunset or another sunrise. This personality, I find, is exemplified by the people who work to maintain and run it 24 hours a day, seven days per week, and 365 days per year.

Mackinac Bridge workers do such a fantastic job that they annually draw praise from inspectors who examine many other bridges nationwide. The point has often been made that the Big Mac is cared for in a way that is far superior to other bridges that are inspected.

So if you've crossed the bridge, seen it from the shore or are only reading about it in these pages, please join me in dedicating this work to the people who take care of the bridge at the Straits of Mackinac.

For if you've collected a fare, painted the steel, answered the phone, performed accounting work, driven a plow, escorted a truck, placed cones on the roadway, or done any of the other jobs at the Mackinac Bridge – then this book is for you.

The excellent care you have taken of the greatest symbol of the state of Michigan has given it the spectacular personality it enjoys today.

I salute you!

Mike Fornes
April, 2007

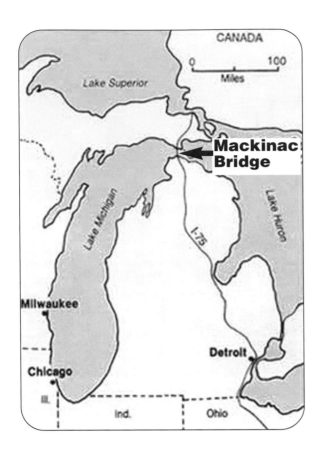

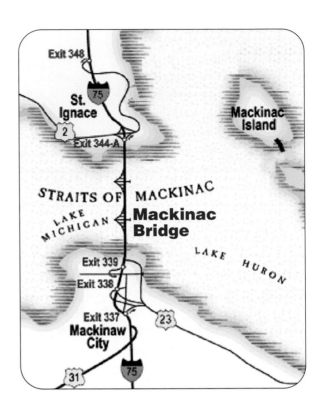

Is it Mackinaw or Mackinac?

Everything — from the Straits, to the island, to the bridge, to the town — that contains either Mackinac or Mackinaw, is pronounced with an "AW" sound at the end.

The Indian name for the area, Michinnimakinong, means "Land of the Great Turtle." When the French arrived in 1715, they spelled it Michilimackinac, but even though they spelled it with an "AC," they still pronounced it "AW."

The British arrived and took over the fort in 1761, and changed the spelling to an English ending of "AW," and the name was shortened to Mackinaw.

The French kept their "AC", and everything north of Mackinaw City still uses that spelling. Mackinaw City, Mackinaw Township and the U.S. Coast Guard cutter Mackinaw are amoung the references below the bridge that uses the "AW" ending. A Mackinaw coat, a Mackinaw boat and fresh Mackinaw whitefish are some others.

Regardless of the spelling, the pronunciation of "AC" is the same as "AW" — only the peninsulas that each spelling represents are different.

Before the Bridge

Before the Mackinac Bridge was opened in 1957, the Michigan Department of Transportation operated a ferry system between Mackinaw City and St. Ignace that took passengers and vehicles across the Straits of Mackinac.

The State Highway Department started ferry service in the Straits area in 1923 in response to demand for service. By the last year of operation, the ferries transported just under 900,000 vehicles.

Though passengers then knew no other way, they could not have predicted how a bridge would impact the lives of those making the crossing. For some, the boat trip was an annual event to be endured over a period of 24 hours, for lines backed up as much as 20 miles in either direction. Today, citizens of Mackinaw City or St. Ignace sometimes use the bridge to commute to work, to school or for recreation and use the bridge each day and sometimes have several crossings in a single day.

Traffic line-ups mostly occurred during holiday periods such as Memorial Day, the week surrounding the July 4th holiday, sometimes the entire month of August and Labor Day weekend. Severe storms could also back up traffic until the boats began moving once again.

But no time of year summarized the frustration of motorists crossing the Straits more than during

The ferry City of Petoskey is ready for a full load of vehicles at the State Dock in Mackinaw City.

firearm deer hunting season.

At its peak in the 1950s, the Michigan Department of Transportation utilized five boats on the route that had to be manned by full crews 24 hours per day. This meant rounding up the laid-off summer personnel and replacing those who would not or could not return.

If a boat did not have a full crew, the U.S. Coast Guard did not permit it to leave the dock. Replacing a crew member was not simply a matter of recruiting a warm body. Each position was certified and the individual employee had to have a certificate to fill the vacant position. There were approximately 325 employees on the five boats and anywhere from 4 percent to 6 percent would simply disappear or call in sick. In addition, pursers and dockmen had to be lined up along with office and warehouse personnel. In all, about 470 employees had to be pressed into service for peak season operation during hunting season.

During the busiest period, which in those days began about Nov. 11 and continued on until the morning of Nov. 15, it is estimated that some 16 persons per day were recruited, hired, fired, promoted and demoted. There was constant turmoil and change in getting people back to work for a short period after they had been laid off just two months before. Without the employees, the boats could not operate.

During the last deer season before the bridge, November of 1956, there was a 23-mile line-up of cars coming north that stretched 15 miles on Old US 27 and eight miles on US 31.

Those who waited in traffic lines beyond the Mackinaw City limits will remember the adventures of heading off into the woods to answer nature's call. Some had nighttime encounters with skunks or porcupines that lurked nearby hoping to get fed by motorists who dumped trash and leftover food in the ditch. Many slept during the waits for movement as another boat loaded up, and kids sometimes had to awaken dad to get going again, or the cars behind would pass them up in the darkness.

The docks were a constant area of confrontation, if not combat.

On the Mackinaw City side, 800 to 1,000 vehicles could be accommodated on the docking area. By the time hunters reached this point and had paid their fare to get on the ferry, they were no longer in the pleasant, jovial mood in which they began their trip. Many had been in line for six or seven hours already on the highway, but now would have to wait another six or seven hours to clear the dock.

Another "full house" at Mackinaw City's State Dock, home of the MDOT car ferries that provided the link between Michigan's upper and lower peninsulas.

Sometimes they would get the impression that the dockmaster was favoring one line over another and all hell would break loose. Yet even this alleged unfairness was child's play compared to their reaction if they thought some VIP was bucking the line. More than one car and its occupants nearly ended up in the Straits when irate hunters thought they were being cheated.

Cars could not be left unattended on the docks or in the line-ups approaching the docks. Movement was frequent, if not constant, and an unattended car was quickly pushed onto the shoulder. Service stations were equipped with hoses to the gas pumps that were as long as 100 feet so that cars could be fueled while remaining in line as they passed the station. Besides the threat of running out of gas, filling the tank on the Lower Peninsula side was important because gasoline was considerably more expensive in the U.P. in those days.

In an era before fast food preparation and quick

The City of Munising, a Michigan Department of Transportation car ferry, in service with the Mackinac Bridge nearing completion in the distance

carry-out service, hunters were fair game for peddlers of smoked fish or pasties wrapped in newspaper. Sandwiches, cheese, crackers and sundry edibles were brought out for sale, sometimes priced far above market value. Hawkers of souvenirs and trinkets took advantage of the hunters' early good nature and filled their pocketbooks from the northbound travelers. Occasionally, there were more severe incidents when hunters "lost" their wallets, and the ferry service was often on the receiving end of calls complaining about the shabby treatment of the travelers.

Deer hunters, often the happiest people alive on their trip northbound, had to endure the return trip in the same long lines north and west of St. Ignace. By then they were often bearded, tired, broke and hung over, and many had no deer to show for their efforts. For others, the entire process became a great adventure, especially for children of families who were on vacation. Just the sight of the ferryboats or at last seeing the Straits after enduring hours of waiting remains a treasured memory of many trips to the wilds of the north for fishing, camping and sightseeing trips.

The same trips take place today, but cross the Straits of Mackinac via the bridge that allows the same passage in less than ten minutes. The "Miracle Bridge at Mackinac" signifies joy and wonder to many, a landmark of the beginning of a great journey or perhaps a destination in itself. To others, the bridge can represent moments of unprecedented vistas, fear,

The St. Ignace State Dock, full of southbound passengers heading home.

anticipation and wonder all at once.

The Mackinac Bridge has seen comedy and sadness, glory and tragedy, life and death, exhilaration and horror. It is a symbol of the state of Michigan, and has encapsulated many aspects of life in the north country while enduring weather extremes, human nature and the forces of mechanical engineering, routine maintenance and added improvements.

Day-to-day life on the bridge can range from the mundane to the newsworthy. This is the story of 50 years of the normal, the unusual, the behind-the-scenes and the most public moments the Big Mac has experienced since opening on Nov. 1, 1957.

The car ferry Vacationland in its last year of service on the Straits, 1957. It was the largest, most modern ferry built for the route between Mackinaw City and St. Ignace and could load vehicles from either end and be piloted from either end. After being sold for scrap, it sank in a powerful Pacific Ocean storm while being towed to China and now rests in nearly two miles of water.

2
The Vision

Years ago, there was no shortage of plans for linking Michigan's two peninsulas. A floating tunnel was suggested in 1920 by Horatio Earle, Michigan's first state highway commissioner.

Another proposal involved building a series of causeways and bridges from Cheboyan to Bois Blanc Island to Round Island across the western tip of Mackinac Island and then across to St. Ignace.

Each plan failed because financial and physical problems seemed insurmountable.

In 1934 Murray D. Van Wagoner, then Democratic State Highway Commissioner, insisted that the Michigan legislature create a Mackinac Straits Bridge Authority to study the feasibility of a bridge.

In 1940 the Authority reported to the legislature that a bridge at the Straits was feasible. One year later, Van Wagoner became governor and during his administration a $1 million causeway was built as the northern approach to the proposed bridge, reaching one-mile south into the Straits from St. Ignace.

Van Wagoner was defeated in 1942, and no further action was taken. The United States had, by this time, entered into World War II. There weren't enough funds, workers or materials to build a bridge because everything was being put into the war effort.

In 1947, the war over, the legislature terminated the Bridge Authority.

G. Mennen Williams, a young Navy veteran, was nominated on the Democratic ticket for governor despite having never before run for elective office. Williams promised to revive the Mackinac Bridge project if elected. He was chosen governor in November, 1948.

G. Mennen Williams

In 1949, Williams appointed the Inter-Peninsula Communications Commission to study the bridge question and other problems arising out of the separation of the two peninsulas. The Commission, headed by John McCarthy, head of the Michigan Public Service Commission, brought the bridge studies out of the Highway Department files and reported again that the bridge was feasible.

Gov. Williams recommended in 1950 that a Mackinac Bridge Authority be re-established, with power to build a bridge. Democrats and Republicans in the legislature joined to re-establish the Authority, but denied it the power to go beyond studying the question. Members of the Authority were appointed by Williams, who retained three engineers to study the project.

In 1951 the Authority reported to the legislature that a bridge at the Straits was feasible from all standpoints — engineering, financial and economic.

Williams again recommended in 1952 that the Authority be empowered to act, and the legislature passed a bill specifying that the bridge must be financed by revenue bonds without cost to the state and without incurring any public indebtedness.

Dr. David B. Steinman, 63, was named as consulting engineer for the Mackinac project in 1953, and Glenn B. Woodruff was named as associate consultant.

Also in 1953, Williams, Sen. Prentiss M. Brown, Charles T. Fisher Jr., and members of the Mackinac Bridge Authority met in New York City with a group of investment bankers. Williams told the bankers that the bridge would provide "a new Northwest Passage" and that "the great Atlantic East will be joined with the wheat and oil fields of Canada."

The bankers were impressed, but the bond market was "soft." Economic conditions were not ripe for a bond issue of nearly $100 million. On the advice of the bond counsel, the Authority asked the legislature to demonstrate the good faith of the state by paying the annual maintenance cost of the bridge out of state highway funds. The legislature agreed that $417,000 per year be diverted from highway funds for bridge maintenance — on the condition that the bonds be sold by Dec. 31, 1953.

With this assurance of state support, the sale of the bonds was arranged by mid-December. However, the bridge was almost stopped when Michigan Sen. Haskell L. Nichols, a Republican from Jackson who had voted against the bridge, filed a lawsuit in the Michigan Supreme Court asking for an injunction to prevent approval of the bond sale by the State Administrative Board. The lawsuit was filed 24 hours before the scheduled sale of the bonds. Had this move succeeded, the $417,000 appropriation would have lapsed and the bridge would have been set back at least a year, and possibly for many years.

The court refused the injunction, and later, after a hearing, upheld the Administrative Board's approval of the bridge's financing.

Prentiss M. Brown, "father" of the Mackinac Bridge, partnered with Charles T. Fisher Jr. and Mackinac Island's Grand Hotel owner W. Stewart Woodfill to sell the Mackinac Bridge project to legislators and investors.

The idea of a bridge at Mackinac had become a political football in the state of Michigan, with Republicans and Democrats eternally disagreeing on whether the bridge should be built and how it should be funded. The Authority sold bonds to privately finance the project. The cost of the bridge was $96,400,033.33 and was paid for with a certified cashier's check. This was accomplished by the leadership and genius of Prentiss M. Brown, known as "the father of the Mackinac Bridge." The bond issue was retired July 1, 1986.

The Detroit architectural firm of Harley, Ellington and Day's conceptual drawing of the toll plaza & Administration Building.

Note the surveyor's towers in these two photos, for the ground-breaking ceremony held in St. Ignace (above) on May 7, 1954 and in Mackinaw City (below) on May 8. They were the only signs of construction for the mammoth project at the time.

Groundbreaking ceremonies were held in St. Ignace on May 7, 1954 and in Mackinaw City on May 8. Large crowds attended the festivities on both sides of the bridge. Construction began immediately, and although the work on the water shut down each winter, it continued on the mainland with crews readying bridge sections that were brought out by barge in the spring and summer to be lifted into place.

The bridge was completed on time, on budget and with private financing through the sale of bonds.

The ferryboats were charging an average of $3.40 per car and passengers when the boats stopped running on Nov. 1, 1957.

These aerial photos of the St. Ignace highway interchange were taken before Interstate 75 was built. Motorists could exit east (above) to St. Ignace, or loop around and head west on US 2. The top photo is looking south, towards the bridge. In those days, you drove through downtown St. Ignace to head north to Sault Ste. Marie.

David Steinman grew up selling newspapers in the shadow of the Brooklyn Bridge and told fellow newsboys that, "Someday I was going to build bridges like the famous structure that towered above us. They laughed at me."

Years later it was apparent that Steinman knew how to build bridges – his firm had been involved in the building of more than 400 bridges on five continents throughout the world. A veritable genius, he had earned his doctorate degree in engineering at the age of 19 from Columbia University and was awarded honorary doctoral degrees from 22 other universities.

He designed bridge foundations to support the superstructure and any live load it would carry by a safety factor of four. The steel superstructure, in turn, would withstand wind pressure of 50 pounds per square foot, or wind velocities up to 600 miles per hour. In the 1950s, the highest wind velocity recorded to date at the Straits of Mackinac was 78 miles-per-hour.

Years later, on May 9, 2003, the highest wind speed yet recorded on the bridge occurred at 4:08 p.m. The anemometer read 124 mph.

Dr. David B. Steinman - engineer, author and poet.

Steinman was quite quotable for the media and spoke with an exacting, authoritative tone. He wrote poetry about his crown jewel, the Mackinac Straits Bridge.

Prentiss M. Brown with Irene Steinman and the plaque dedicated to her late husband. David B. Steinman died in 1960, three years after completing the bridge.

During a study of prospective Mackinac Bridge engineers, the Bridge Authority posed a question to the candidates:

Question: "Gentlemen, what would happen to one of your foundations if a boat loaded with ore crashed into it?"
Answer: "The boat would sink with a serious loss of life."

Dr. David B. Steinman gave that answer, and got the job over Othmar H. Amman, a Swedish-born New Yorker, and Glenn B. Woodruff of San Francisco. Amman had built the George Washington and Whitestone bridges in New York and many others throughout the country, and Woodruff had participated in the design of several structures in California including the Oakland Bay Bridge.

The Mackinaw City highway interchange takes shape to serve bridge traffic. Note the railroad yard to the right, today the site of hotels and shopping areas.

The Golden Gate Bridge only cost $36 million to build in 1937.

But Steinman knew that he faced challenges far different from those seen in San Francisco Bay. In the Straits of Mackinac, the winds and waves would be worse, the suspended span longer and the water would freeze into ice that could be ten feet thick during build-ups that threatened to sweep clear anything left on the surface.

Another situation that Steinman resolved to avoid was that of the Tacoma Narrows Bridge disaster. Situated on the Tacoma Narrows in Puget Sound, near the city of Tacoma, Washington, the bridge had only been open for traffic a few months when trouble occurred.

On Nov. 7, 1940, at approximately 11 a.m., the first Tacoma Narrows suspension bridge collapsed due to wind-induced vibrations.

Dr. David B. Steinman was paid $3.5 million for bridge engineering fees, and hired a staff of 350 engineers to solve the design problems he faced in building the Mackinac Bridge. His design was built to withstand far more wind than had destroyed the Tacoma Narrows Bridge, insuring that a disaster like the one that occurred there would never take place at the Straits of Mackinac.

The complete story of that disaster is told with photographs in Chapter 19.

Construction is ongoing on the Administration Building in 1956.

An aerial view of the office facilities. The maintenance building is not yet in place.

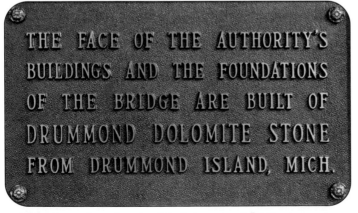

THE FACE OF THE AUTHORITY'S BUILDINGS AND THE FOUNDATIONS OF THE BRIDGE ARE BUILT OF DRUMMOND DOLOMITE STONE FROM DRUMMOND ISLAND, MICH.

This plaque describes the Administration Building's construction materials, also used for the bridge foundation.

The completed Administration Building, ready for occupancy. On June 26, 1983, it was re-named the Brown-Fisher Administration Building.

Houses were removed and streets blocked as the bridge's south approach was built through Mackinaw City.

This view of Exit 339 at Mackinaw City looks barren compared to the busy community that exists there today.

This ramp, Exit 338 off I-75, still takes southbound traffic onto US 23 to Cheboygan.

Visitors gathered on the Mackinaw City shoreline to watch the bridge take shape. Missing sections made the bridge appear as a mirage until the link was completed between the two peninsulas.

Ironworkers performed magical feats in building the bridge. Modern engineering made it look easy, but it wasn't easy.

An artist's concept of the underwater design of the bridge caissons. Approximately two-thirds of the bridge's mass is beneath the surface of the Straits, not visible to everyday traffic.

Whole sections of the bridge were constructed on land, floated out on barges and raised into place.

Work on the box beams, causeway and pier supports all came after the suspension cables were stretched above the two towers to the anchor piers.

The Bridge at Mackinac

By David B. Steinman

In the land of Hiawatha,
Where the white man gazed with awe
At a paradise divided
By the Straits of Mackinac

Men are dredging, drilling, blasting,
Battling tides around the clock,
Through the depths of icy water,
Driving caissons down to rock.

Fleets of freighters bring their cargoes
From the forges and the kilns;
Stones and steel - ten thousand barge-loads -
From the quarries, mines, and mills.

Now the towers, mounting skyward,
Reach the heights of airy space.
Hear the rivet-hammers ringing,
Joining steel in strength and grace.

High above the swirling currents,
Parabolic strands are strung;
From the cables, packed with power,
Wonder-spans of steel are hung.

Generations dreamed the crossing;
Doubters shook their heads in scorn.
Brave men vowed that they would build it -
From their faith a bridge was born.

There it spans the miles of water,
Speeding millions on their way -
Bridge of vision, hope and courage,
Portal to a brighter day.

3

Michigan is One

As construction rushed to completion in the fall of 1957, many preparations were under way for various "firsts" that were bound to occur. People wanted to be the first to cross the Mackinac Bridge in some particular manner or type of vehicle. Michigan Gov. G. Mennen Williams would have the honor of being the first to cross and pay the toll, but all the rest would follow.

Unofficially Amelia Cole was the first -- before

The Catsman Company provided cement for construction of the Mackinac Bridge. The firm's office manager was driven across before the bridge opened and achieved the honor of being the first to unofficially cross the "Mighty Mac."

everyone else – to cross the bridge, and rode across in the first vehicle to drive the whole five miles of the bridge before it was finished.

The date was Sept. 10, 1957.

"In a construction like that, women were never permitted," Cole told the Cheboygan Daily Tribune 45 years later. "Things are changing just a little bit, but have you ever heard of a woman (on such structures) that has been one of the original crossers or has anything to do with it?"

How the crossing came to pass was not something Cole had planned or anticipated.

As the office manager for the Catsman Company, which had a contract for the cement part of the construction, it was part of her job to help prepare for the following day's work.

"Every night I had to go out and check with the engineer for what they were going to need for the next day," said Cole.

So on Sept. 10, 1957, at about 5 p.m. she checked with Superintendent Eugene Yanko of the Merritt-Chapman Scott Company to see if it would be possible yet to have one of the Catsman Company's trucks driven all the way across because it had to be in St. Ignace at 6 p.m. the next day. She was told that the bridge was still not ready, and that the truck should be sent over on a ferry.

While talking and joking around with the guys, she noticed a car parked in a funny location at the bridge, she said.

"I did not know I was not going back to my office," Cole said.

Yanko told her she might as well get in the car, and didn't leave her a choice, she said. Gordon Dallas, consulting engineer for the D. B Steinman Company, was at the wheel.

"(Yanko) pushed me in the car and said 'you're going to be the first person across this bridge,'" said Cole. "I didn't know what I was supposed to do."

But the bridge was not the smooth, unfettered concrete surface it is now. Wooden planks covered gaps in the bridge deck, which was still under construction at the time.

"There were eight places with planks," said Cole.

"They were only for the engineers and people who worked on the bridge to cross. The abyss – there was nothing at all to connect that bridge to these eight planked crossings. Instead of heading for my office, he started across these planks and scared me out of my wits."

Cole said it was as much as 200 feet down to the water beneath the makeshift span.

That first crossing took 90 minutes, because construction equipment on the bridge had to be moved out of the way, she added.

The men who were working on the bridge went along with the first vehicular crossing over what had been designed for foot traffic because they liked doing tricks of that sort, said Cole.

"The fellas on the bridge were swell," Cole remarked.

Once they reached the St. Ignace side, the "fellas" wanted to celebrate at a local tavern, and took Cole along.

Amelia Cole was the first woman to cross the bridge in an automobile...

D. B. STEINMAN
CONSULTING ENGINEER

D. B. STEINMAN
W. E. JOYCE
J. LONDON
R. M. BOYNTON
C. H. GRONQUIST

ROEBLING BUILDING
117 LIBERTY STREET
NEW YORK 6, N. Y.
BARCLAY 7-2665
CABLE ADDRESS
"STEINMANCE" N.Y.

September 18, 1957

Mrs. O. C. Cole
C/o Catsman Company
Mackinaw City, Michigan

Dear Mrs. Cole:

I am very glad to have the interesting clipping enclosed with your letter of September 12. Please accept my congratulations on being the first woman to cross the Mackinac Bridge. I am sure it was a thrilling experience.

With kind regards,

Faithfully yours,

D B Steinman

DBS:al   D. B. STEINMAN

...and then later received a congratulatory letter from the engineer who designed the Mackinac Bridge.

"I had never been in a bar in my life," Cole said. "I was stuck in St. Ignace. I didn't have a handkerchief or anything with me."

Apparently, the fellas let time get away from them and Cole almost missed the last boat back to the Lower Peninsula.

"They had to hold the 11:30 p.m. ferry so someone would get me there in order to get back to Mackinaw," said Cole.

It was after midnight when she arrived back in Mackinaw City. But word had already spread like wildfire about her feat.

"I didn't realize when I rode to Mackinaw City that there would be a lot of people there," Cole said. "The telephone rang. We were up all night and the next day talking to reporters. For four days we couldn't do anything but telephone."

The story appeared in newspapers across the nation, she said.

After that, every time Cole saw the Mackinac Bridge looming above the village it reminded her of that heart-pounding ride across.

"That was one of the most important things that happened in my life as far as I'm concerned," said Cole. "It's an occurrence that cannot be repeated. No one else can do it."

About one week after Cole's ride across the bridge, two St. Ignace women claimed to be the first to walk across the span, also before it officially opened. Mellina Hill and Molly Boulanger told the Associated Press that starting from the St. Ignace side, they reached Mackinaw City in two hours. The women said they had permission to walk across the still uncompleted bridge, but declined to say who gave them the go-ahead. They said they returned to St. Ignace by ferry.

Mackinaw City became a hub of excitement in the months leading up to the opening of the bridge. This photo shows the expanse that was the Mackinaw City railroad yard.

Newspapers of the day heralded the new bridge as a uniting factor for Michigan.

On Nov. 1, 1957, traffic officially opened on the Mackinac Bridge.

A huge story, the event attracted 150 newspapermen from throughout Michigan and neighboring states that included Wisconsin, Illinois, Ohio, Indiana, New York and Ontario. The Associated Press and United Press International opened offices in the area, and Life Magazine, the New York Times and Chicago Tribune sent reporters. Detroit radio station WJR sent a mobile broadcasting unit in a specially equipped bus to beam the proceedings back to Detroit for broadcast throughout the Midwest.

Fifty members of the Michigan Legislature accepted invitations, the Cheboygan Daily Tribune reported.

A motorcade of cars from every county in the Upper Peninsula formed at St. Ignace, where a convention of the Upper Peninsula Development Bureau was held to coincide with the bridge opening.

With media and the legislators riding in special buses, the throng drove out onto the bridge for the inspection tour.

Speeches were made on Pier 22, the bridge's north anchor block, declaring the Straits to be conquered at last for automobile traffic. Another stop was made at center span, where Michigan Gov. G. Mennen Williams presented cuff links to several distinguished

Gov. Williams starts across the bridge, driven by Larry Rubin for the first leg. His wife, Nancy, took over later.

Detroit's WJR Radio interviewed Gov. Williams and Prentiss M. Brown using the station's remote studio bus.

Each county in the Upper Peninsula sent a car to represent their first crossing. Escanaba's car proclaimed it as "Home of the Walleye," welcomed by fare collector Wally Burrell.

leaders, including David B. Steinman, Prentiss M. Brown and George Bishop, who had retired after 36 years as president of the Upper Peninsula Development Bureau.

Williams also passed out copies of his Bridge Day proclamation to members of the Bridge Authority, Highway Commissioner John C. Mackie, Steinman and others. He then handed a packet of letters to the St. Ignace postmaster to mail, postmarked for the day of the bridge opening. The letters were addressed to the governors of the other 47 states inviting them to the bridge dedication to be held in June, 1958.

Chairman Brown read a letter announcing the decision of the U.S. Postal Service to issue a Straits Bridge commemorative stamp at the time of the ded-ication.

Meanwhile, the ferries began their final trips. At 1:45 p.m. the City of Petoskey arrived at St. Ignace and began an open house, attended by many relatives and friends of the ferry crewmen. At Dock No. 3 in St. Ignace, a program was held in honor of the ferry crews and dockmen. Mayors of the cities after whom the ferries were named gave plaques to the captains of their communities' namesakes.

Mayor Quincy Leslie gave a plaque to Captain Pat Gallagher of the ferry City of Cheboygan. Other mayors or their representatives gave plaques to captains of the City of Petoskey and the City of Munising. Mayor Al Phillips of St. Ignace gave a plaque to the captain of the ferry Straits of Mackinac.

Nov. 1, 1957 – The last day of service for the Michigan Department of Transportation's ferryboats traveling between the upper and lower peninsulas of the state.

With the ferries stopped and the bridge barricaded, cars were lined up at the bridge from the north and the south. Traffic was waiting at the St. Ignace end for a mile and a half, and at the Mackinaw City approach for two miles.

The first official bridge fare was to be paid by Williams, who was driven across by his wife, Nancy. At St. Ignace, scores of legislators, newspapermen and official guests waited for the official opening.

At 2 p.m., Williams arrived from Mackinaw City in a limousine in front of the toll plaza at the north end of the bridge. Waiting for him was Chairman Prentiss M. Brown of the Mackinac Bridge Authority, with a borrowed toll collector's cap on his head.

The chairman held out his hand and the governor presented an oversized check made out for $3.25. Ceremonial protocol aside, everyone crossing the bridge had to pay and there have never been arrangements made to accept a check at the toll booths. But this was left for the accountants to decide, as Brown

then nodded to a State Trooper who relayed the word through the radio in his car to open the bridge. A State Police officer waiting at Mackinaw City received the notice to remove barriers from the traffic lanes, and cars began streaming across.

Michigan's First Lady, Nancy Williams, was at the wheel when the governor's car arrived at the toll booth.

Michigan's governor paid the first toll by check, which took fare collectors by surprise.

That was the culmination of 70 years of talking and dreaming about a Straits bridge, of discouraging attempts in the legislature and in Congress to get the bridge approved, of efforts to raise the funds, and finally of a four-year construction program necessary for the world's longest and costliest (to date) bridge.

When the bridge was opened to traffic, the Straits ferry fleet stopped forever. One era opened in history as another ended.

When the barriers were removed, there was a traffic jam on the bridge as cars arrived faster than toll collectors could take their money.

After the ceremonies, traffic streamed across the bridge to the Upper Peninsula.

The car that was the first fare-paying vehicle to cross the bridge was on display for some time near the toll booths before it was permanently located at a Grand Rapids museum. The owner, a jazz-band drummer from Chicago named Al Carter who made a hobby of being first at various events, at one point wanted to sink it off the bridge's center span but environmentalists blocked the plan.

Boy Scouts handed motorists their souvenir crossing cards just before they reached the toll booths at St. Ignace.

STATE OF MICHIGAN
MACKINAC BRIDGE AUTHORITY
THIS IS TO CERTIFY THAT

CROSSED THE MACKINAC BRIDGE ON NOV. 1, 1957, THE FIRST DAY IT WAS OPEN FOR TRAFFIC.

Prentiss M. Brown

Chairman Mackinac Bridge Authority

Souvenir crossing cards were given to first-day customers of the bridge.

On the south side, motorists arrived in Mackinaw City, having crossed over from St. Ignace for the first time by bridge.

With the bridge open, a less joyous program began of bidding goodbye to the ferry crewmen, some of whom started work the next day for the Bridge Authority in various jobs.

The Vacationland was the last ferry to cross, arriving in Mackinaw City with a full load of invited guests and newsmen covering the angle of the ferry system ending service. The start of the trip was made in good weather, but fog quickly closed in. However, the weather was quite unseasonably warm and pleasant for the first day of November. Gov. Williams even took the wheel for part of the trip.

When the Vacationland eased into the Mackinaw City dock, hundreds of people were waiting to watch the final ferry arrival. The Mackinaw City High School Band played vigorously. A speaking stand was set up on the dock and a program was held there similar to the one honoring ferry crewmen in St. Ignace. Mackinaw City Village President Neil Downing presided, and told the crowd "the bridge makes the state physically united as well as governmentally one." Downing presented a scroll to Captain Frank Nelson of the Vacationland.

Some motorists continued to arrive at the dock to cross the Straits, but were told to go to the bridge. The ferries were tied up for good, and the Mackinac Straits Bridge was now open for business.

Michigan was indeed one.

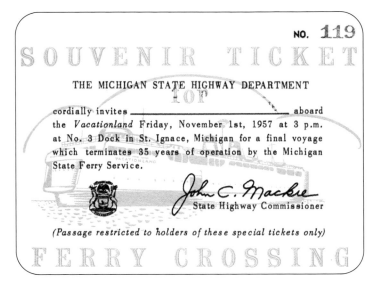

SOUVENIR TICKET

NO. 119

THE MICHIGAN STATE HIGHWAY DEPARTMENT

TOP

cordially invites _____ aboard the *Vacationland* Friday, November 1st, 1957 at 3 p.m. at No. 3 Dock in St. Ignace, Michigan for a final voyage which terminates 35 years of operation by the Michigan State Ferry Service.

John C. Mackie
State Highway Commissioner

(Passage restricted to holders of these special tickets only)

FERRY CROSSING

Commemorative souvenir tickets were handed out to the last passengers on the Vacationland, ending more than three decades of service at the Straits.

The ferry Vacationland was packed with invited guests for its last trip across the Straits.

4
Dedication Days

After the Mackinac Bridge was opened for business and completed its first winter of use, plans were set for the formal dedication festival, held over three days from June 26 – 28, 1958. The dates were a Thursday, Friday and Saturday.

It was billed at the time as the greatest celebration ever held in Michigan. It was on such a large scale that the principal events were spread out over three towns with other activities at Petoskey and Sault Ste. Marie.

On Thursday and Friday, activities were under way at Mackinaw City, St. Ignace and Cheboygan. The Cheboygan Daily Tribune reported that Mackinaw and St. Ignace both held military displays, fireworks and other important events both days. The Agarama agricultural show and sports show were held at Cheboygan both days. A legislative reception and queens' banquet were held at Cheboygan Friday night.

On Saturday, activities were centered on the dedication, which was held near the center of the bridge.

A parade was held at St. Ignace on Thursday and the Mackinaw City parade was Friday.

A magnificent fireworks display was set off on both Thursday and Friday nights at both Mackinaw City and St. Ignace. Each city had its display at the Mackinac Bridge shoreline. The St. Ignace display was first each night at 9:30 p.m., with Mackinaw City's starting at 10 p.m. In all, 600 varieties of fireworks were used and touched off 12 American flag displays.

Military displays and other exhibits were located on the state ferry docks at Mackinaw City and St. Ignace.

Dick Campbell and Joe Marchand stretched a green ribbon from Mackinaw City to St. Ignace to symbolize the joining of Michigan's two peninsulas.

Itinerary 83 County Queens of Michigan

Friday—June 27, 1958

1:00 PM   Parade—Sault Ste. Marie Michigan.

3:15 PM   Parade St. Ignace

4:00 PM   Parade Mackinaw City

5:15 PM   Parade Cheboygan

Saturday—June 28, 1958

9:30 AM   UP Queens parade behind military units— St. Ignace
LP Queens parade behind military units— Mackinaw City

11:00 AM   Miss Michigan leads UP Queen motorcade from St. Ignace, and Mrs. Michigan leads LP Queen motorcade from Mackinaw City onto Bridge to North Anchor Block.

11:30 AM   Formal Dedicatory Ceremonies Begin

This program may be subject to slight change.

Mackinac Bridge Souvenir Book

This book is being sold by civic groups throughout the participating communities to help defray expenses of the Festival. This excellent editorial and pictorial presentation of the Mackinac Bridge will be a lasting memento of this historical event. Don't delay—buy your copy today.

MACKINAC BRIDGE GLASS

FREE

Souvenir frosted tumblers

To commemorate the official dedication of the new Mackinac Bridge, we are offering this beautiful souvenir glass with the purchase of ten gallons or more of Leonard gasoline at any Leonard Community Service Station.

MACKINAC BRIDGE

DEDICATION FESTIVAL

PROGRAM

for activities at
MACKINAW CITY
ST. IGNACE
CHEBOYGAN
SAULT STE. MARIE
HARBOR SPRINGS—PETOSKEY
JUNE 26, 27, 28, 1958

Approximately 2,500 men of the armed forces took part in the event. Two hundred National Guardsmen pitched camp at Mackinaw City High School, then located in a downtown neighborhood that today is home to Old School Park, at the intersection of Henry Street and Jamet Street. A destroyer escort and five patrol craft assembled and were joined by three Coast Guard cutters. Helicopter crews demonstrated air-sea rescues. Civil Air Patrol planes landed on the State Dock at Mackinaw in a demonstration of pin-point landing techniques. At night, the ships played their searchlights on the Mackinac Bridge.

The U.S. Coast Guard cutter Mackinaw held an

Mackinaw City's High School Band marched in the Dedication Festival Parade.

open house all three days at St. Ignace.

Military exhibits included the 68-foot Redstone missile that helped launch American satellites into orbit. Nike missiles were also hauled through Mackinaw City and St. Ignace and up to the bridge in daily parades.

The U.S. Army displayed a 40-foot by 80-foot plastic bubble tent intended for use as a shelter in battle areas.

Scores of jet and propeller-driven planes zoomed over the Straits.

Three hours were set aside on Thursday and Friday from noon until 3 p.m. for parades that were the longest and most beautiful ever held to date in the area.

The Tribune said that 140 units were accepted for the Mackinaw City parade, which started from the high school with units falling in line from assembly points on side streets. A reviewing stand was set up on the south side of Central Avenue near the tennis courts, near where the north entrance to the Mackinaw Crossings

shopping complex is located today.

The parade continued on to US 23 and Old US 27 and dispersed in the southern part of the city. The parade was led by color guards of the Army, Air Force, Marines, Navy, Coast Guard and Civil Air Patrol. Approximately 20 bands played, including the 5th Army Band.

Numerous queens took part, representing all Michigan counties and festivals throughout the state. Among them were Miss Mackinaw City, Miss St. Ignace, Miss Michigan, Mrs. Michigan and Miss Armed Forces. Also present were the Michigan Apple Queen, the Michigan Bean Queen, the Michigan Cherry Queen and the Michigan Dairy Princess.

Oxen teams, antique autos, motorcycle units and Detroit mounted policemen represented varieties of transportation. Many beautiful floats were involved, including local entries from nearly all area communities in the northern part of the state.

Various commemorative events took place during

Diane Krueger was "Miss Mackinaw City" and rode in the Dedication Festival Parade with queens from all 83 Michigan counties and those representing many festivals.

Miss St. Ignace, Lenore Allen, represented the gateway city to the Upper Peninsula.

Mrs. Michigan, Barbara Dolan, of Greenville, Mich., led the Lower Peninsula queens on the parade route.

Dr. David B. Steinman and his wife, Irene, were guests of honor in the parade.

The arrivals of explorer Jean Nicolet and missionary Fr. Jacques Marquette were re-enacted using birch-bark canoes, contrasting frontier methods of transportation with the modern day marvel of the Mackinac Bridge.

The Oldsmobile Company furnished a white convertible for each county queen, festival queen and other dignitaries while at the Mackinac Bridge Dedication Festival in June, 1958. The queens were escorted across the Mackinac Bridge by the Detroit Police Commando Unit Motorcycle Squad. Mrs. Michigan was in the lead car for the Lower Peninsula contingent, and Miss Michigan led the Upper Peninsula queens.

the celebration. On Friday, the trip of Jean Nicolet, first European to visit the Straits, was re-enacted. Two champion canoeists set out from the beach at Mackinaw City at 10 a.m. in a birch-bark canoe, while another laden with beaver skins was paddled from the Upper Peninsula shore by two Indian canoeists. The two canoes met under the center of the bridge.

A marker was unveiled at the Michilimackinac State Park to commemorate the establishment of a fort at Mackinaw City by the French in 1715.

Tractor skill driving, six-horse hitches, amateur horse racing and Miss Rodeo America were some of the featured acts at the Cheboygan Agarama, which also promised drill teams, folk dancers, 4-H demonstrations and the state's top six talent acts.

This was followed by a tourist sport show with Indian ceremonies and rituals, marksmanship demonstrations by gun experts, archery shooting, a demonstration by Ben Hardesty – world casting champion, and tumblers and trampoline stars from Michigan State University.

Mackinaw City was reportedly "full of people" by Tuesday night of the dedication week and traffic was already heavy on northbound highways. An 80-man State Police detail was sent north to help control traffic at the Straits and was headquartered on the Vacationland ferry at the State Dock. Twenty-four of the Troopers were allotted to help the Cheboygan State Police detachment in extra traffic patrols.

To top it all off, the Diocese of Grand Rapids issued a letter dispensing the faithful of the Roman Catholic Church from the counties of Cheboygan, Emmet and Otsego from the law of abstinence for Friday, June 27. The Diocese of Marquette likewise issued a similar dispensation covering the counties of Mackinac and Chippewa. This meant that meat could be served and eaten freely by those in attendance at the Mackinac Bridge Dedication Festival.

Bridget Paquet, born on the day construction began on the bridge in 1954, posed on the Mackinaw City float with Mrs. Michigan. Barbara Dolan, at the 1958 dedication.

The June 1958 dedication of the Mackinac Bridge wound up with far worse weather than the actual opening day festivities held the previous November.

Only a comparative few of the thousands of people attending the celebration were able to watch the dedication, held at Pier 22 – the north anchor block of the bridge. It was there that a five-mile length of ribbon was stretched from Mackinaw City at the south end and from the St. Ignace shore to the north. The four-inch ribbon was unwound from large spools and attached to the side view mirrors of the queens' convertibles until the ends met, a process that took 25 minutes. There the ribbons were tied, symbolizing that Michigan's two peninsulas were tied together as one by the bridge.

Access to the Saturday bridge dedication ceremonies was by invitation only. Other visitors were able to hear the proceedings through a public address system set up at exhibit areas in both St. Ignace and Mackinaw City.

The formal ceremonies began at 11:30 a.m., with Prentiss M. Brown serving as the master of ceremonies. An invocation was read by the Rev. Lester J. Maitland. At that point the ribbon tying took place, with Gov. Williams, Brown, Walker Cisler, Mayor Al Phillips of St. Ignace and Mackinaw City Village President Neil Downing all taking part. The queens from Mackinac County, Cheboygan County and Emmet County were on hand with Miss Michigan and Mrs. Michigan.

Many speakers then took the stage, with weather conditions cool and worsening as time went on. Who would have ever predicted that it would have been a more pleasant day the previous November, when the bridge opened, than a date at the end of June?

Speeches were given by Williams, Canada's Secretary of State Henri Courtemanche, David B. Steinman, House Speaker George M. Van Peursem and others. Msgr. James H. Moloney gave the benediction and the VIP guests were then whisked off to a luncheon under skies that were rapidly deteriorating.

It was apparent that a front was closing in, and although the formal dedication concluded at 1 p.m., another dedication was then held at the foot of the bridge on the Mackinaw City side. August Scholle, president of the Michigan AFL-CIO, dedicated a plaque honoring the five workmen who lost their lives during construction of the bridge.

On the heels of the day's events, the storm hit with full force in the Straits area, buffeting displays, crowds of tourists and groups present for the ceremonies with high winds and a brief cloudburst of rain.

It was almost as if Mother Nature had allowed the dedication ceremonies to be celebrated, and then showed a display of fury at man's daring in conquering the Straits with a bridge of steel and concrete.

The bridge didn't even flinch.

Just as the celebration ended on Saturday, a storm whipped through the Straits with high winds that knocked down displays on the State Dock at Mackinaw City. The ceremonies had ended just in time, and dedication traffic was off the bridge before the storm cell hit.

Mackinaw City's float in the Dedication Festival Parade was later displayed on the front lawn of the Mackinaw City Village Hall.

This postmark was issued in commemoration of the dedication of the Mackinac Bridge in 1958.

The bridge's first birthday was celebrated Nov. 1, 1958 at center-span with a giant birthday cake.

5
Michigan's Icon

Once the Mackinac Bridge was completed, it didn't take long before businesses in the Straits Area, in Michigan and throughout America began to realize that the new five-mile bridge was something special. It had displaced San Francisco's Golden Gate Bridge as the longest suspension-span bridge in the world.

But beyond its length, the miracle bridge at Mackinac had united an entire state, joining the upper and lower peninsulas in a way that evoked great pride from both ends of Michigan.

This bridge stood for Michigan, and began to show up in advertisements, on billboards and designs that promoted the state. It became a featured picture on postcards and souvenirs of every description.

From the dedication day of the bridge onward, it was apparent that Michigan's new engineering feat was being recognized as practically the eighth wonder of the world.

The Postmaster General of the United States, Arthur Summerfield, came to the Straits of Mackinac to take part in the Mackinac Bridge Dedication Festival ceremonies. Summerfield was met by more than 300 people at the Pellston Airport and continued to Mackinaw City where he broke ground there for a new post office, spoke at St. Ignace, then gave an address on Mackinac Island where he was the guest of honor at a Grand Hotel luncheon.

Summerfield's presence was due to the issuance of a three-cent Mackinac Bridge stamp that went on sale June 25, 1958. The stamp was used to pay for first-class letter-sized mail sent anywhere in the United States. Both the Mackinaw City and St. Ignace post offices participated in special day-of-issue sales, sending hundreds of thousands of pieces of pre-addressed mail on its way to collectors and dealers bearing the postmark "Mackinac Bridge" and dated June 25.

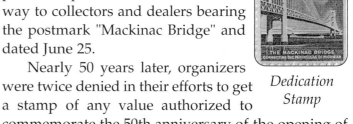

Dedication Stamp

Nearly 50 years later, organizers were twice denied in their efforts to get a stamp of any value authorized to commemorate the 50th anniversary of the opening of the Mackinac Bridge.

According to Susan Godzik, who helped organize a letter-writing campaign after the request was denied for 2007, the Citizen's Advisory Committee of the U.S. Postal Service discussed the idea of a stamp commemorating the five-mile span and rejected it.

"They said they were impressed with all of the support," Godzik said. "Unfortunately, a vast majority of suggestions submitted — including many meritorious and meaningful subjects — cannot result in a stamp."

The Leonard Gasoline Company offered these glasses with a purchase in 1958.

The bridge's likeness was sold on a variety of items, including this serving tray.

A new century brought a new look to Michigan drivers' licenses.

Souvenir plates were sold in local gift shops.

This sign, explaining the bridge's pier structure, stood on the Mackinaw City shoreline for many years and later at St. Ignace.

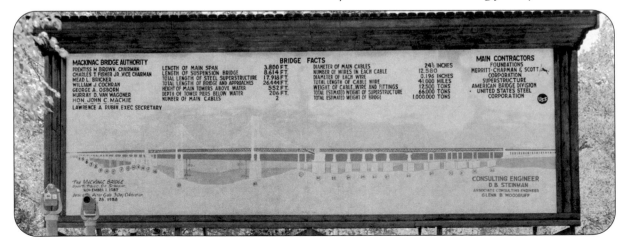

In Michigan, the Mackinac Bridge is universally recognized as the state's icon. The bridge appears on the Michigan quarter, the state's driver's licenses and two of the license plates issued for vehicles. It has an amazing ability to draw tourists who cross over, cross under, photograph and paint it. The bridge's magnetic appeal has extended to well beyond those who rode in the more than 100 million vehicles who have crossed it in the years it has been open to traffic.

Add to that figure the many millions and millions of visitors who have looked at the Big Mac in awe from the shorelines of either peninsula, Mackinac Island, a passing ferry or other vessel.

Karrie White, manager of the Travel Michigan Visitors Welcome Center at Mackinaw City, displays commemorative posters and the 2007 Michigan road maps at the information center.

A panoramic view of the Bridge's architectural beauty from lake level, an image often used on postcards.

Karen Jean Southwell, Miss Michigan (America) 1961, visited the top of the bridge's south tower for a publicity photo.

Dr. and Mrs. David Steinman sent this Christmas card in 1958.

The Song of the Bridge

The light gleams on my strands and bars

In glory when the sun goes down.

I spread a net to hold the stars

And wear the sunset as my crown.

Dr. and Mrs. D. B. Steinman

Christmas, 1958

A Michigan Week celebration featured the Mackinac Bridge in its logo promoting the state in world progress.

A veterans group enjoyed a trip to the top of the bridge towers. The tour is by special arrangement only.

State advertising campaigns invited skiers and snowmobilers to enjoy the north country's winter sports season.

This license plate proclaiming "Great Lakes Splendor" was in use for several years from the turn of the century ...

... and was replaced by this version, touting "Spectacular Peninsulas" in 2007.

Many recreational events have had the Mackinac Bridge as a magnificent backdrop, including the Mackinaw Grand Prix Snowmobile Race, held on the bay at Mackinaw City.

Actress Ann B. Davis, "Alice" from TV's "The Brady Bunch," clowned around while bridge worker Fred Scott was doing some painting on a suspension cable.

Massachusetts Sen. John F. Kennedy posed with Michigan Gov. G. Mennen Williams in 1960 while campaigning for the presidency.

Actor Dan Blocker, "Hoss" from TV's "Bonanza," visited the bridge to film a commercial for Chevy trucks.
"There's somethin' comin ... somethin' big," Hoss said.

Lady Byrd Johnson, wife of President Lyndon Baines Johnson, visited the bridge on her way to the Grand Hotel on Mackinac Island,

Milestone Crossings

Among the many successful and routine crossings made by motorists on the Mackinac Bridge, some very unusual events have taken place.

Famous people have crossed. Marriages have been proposed and marriage ceremonies performed. New lives have begun. Sadly, deaths have occurred as well.

The birth of a child – usually a memorable, happy occasion – can take on a stressful tone when the event occurs outside a hospital.

Now, imagine giving birth on the Mackinac Bridge.

It has happened three times, and two were premature babies born in ambulances en route to the hospital.

On May 11, 1983, Kim Shuman visited her doctor in Kinross, Mich., when she thought she might be having contractions even though she was but six months into her pregnancy.

"I didn't feel well at all," Shuman recalled 24 years later. "The doctor said I should go to the hospital in Petoskey because they had a specialist and the only neo-natal unit in the area at the time if the baby did come early, but he didn't think I would have the baby that day."

Cathy Flores said that she had been with the Kinross Ambulance Corps for about a year and a half when she assisted Shuman in the back of the ambu-

REUNITED - Kim Shuman (left) gave birth prematurely to son Shawn on May 11, 1983 in a Kinross Township Ambulance on Pier 17, the bridge's south anchor block. Cathy Flores (right) delivered the baby, who was only six months along and weighed just 2 pounds, 3 1/2 ounces.

lance as they crossed the Mackinac Bridge. Mary Fletcher was the driver.

"We had our emergency lights on and had crossed already; her problems were very much in evidence," Flores said. "She was in labor and we knew then that we had to get to the nearest hospital, wherever it was."

The decision was made to turn around and head back to St. Ignace to the Mackinac Straits Hospital.

"I told Mary we didn't have much time, and she made a U-turn in a service cut-across on the freeway," Flores continued. "The next thing I knew Mary said we were being assisted by a policeman but it turned out he was pulling us over – said that we couldn't make a U-turn like that unless there was an emergency. I yelled out that we were having a baby in the back if he wanted to help and then he let us go on across."

Within minutes, at 5:10 p.m., the situation intensified.

"I didn't know we were on the bridge," Shuman remembered. "I just knew that the ambulance was bouncing around and then stopped."

"I told Mary to pull over, but she said she couldn't and then said up ahead she would," Flores said of Fletcher's decision to pull off the bridge roadway at Pier 17. "I'd had lots of training, but that was my first baby. It came real fast, real smooth. I didn't think he was alive; he was so tiny and gray. I turned him over and just rubbed his little back, kind of feeling sorry for him. He sort of hiccuped and started screaming and crying, pretty alert for only being six months along."

Shawn Shuman weighed just 2 pounds, 3 1/2 ounces upon arrival at Mackinac Straits Hospital. He was then transported to Little Traverse Hospital (as it was then known) in Petoskey in a mobile incubator.

"It was pretty neat, pretty exciting," Flores summarized.

Anastasia Marie Johnson was the second baby born on the Mackinac Bridge, delivered May 24, 1997.

Her mother, Yvette Johnson, gave birth to her fourth daughter a short time after winning $60 at the slot machines at the Kewadin Shores Casino in St. Ignace.

"It was really scary because the baby wasn't due until July 15," Johnson told the Detroit News.

The Detroit woman was on a three-day casino tour in Northern Michigan when the expectant mother became ill around 3 a.m. When her water broke a doctor was called to the casino.

Dr. George Pramstaller was on duty in the emergency room at Mackinac Straits Hospital and decided to take Johnson to Northern Michigan Hospital in Petoskey, some 50 miles away, because of its neo-natal intensive care unit.

"But I knew we wouldn't make it in time," Pramstaller said.

Anastasia was born about midway across the bridge.

"The delivery went fine, although not as easy as in the controlled setting of a delivery room – that's for sure," he added.

Anastasia weighed in at 3 pounds, 4 ounces and was transferred two days later to Children's Hospital in Detroit where she remained until she gained more weight.

Little is known about a third birth, that bridge officials say took place in a car at mid-span.

While cars, trucks, buses and motorcycles are the usual fares through the tollbooths, imagine what the toll collectors must have wondered the day they saw a scene out of the Old West approaching.

A horse-drawn wagon crossed the bridge on June 30, 1973, part of an Amish family's missionary journey across America.

Roland Church, his wife and their two daughters rode in a Conestoga wagon hitched to two horses at 5 a.m., escorted by a bridge patrol officer. The early crossing, made from the Mackinaw City side to St. Ignace, was planned to avoid possible problems

The first deer to cross the bridge during the 1957 hunting season. Toll booth collectors have counted many since then.

These pranksters staged a photo that turned the tables on a typical hunter.

A common November sight at the toll booths. Bridge fare collectors annually track the number of deer harvested by hunters to approximate the seasonal totals.

between the horses and passing motorists.

The family told the Cheboygan Daily Tribune that they averaged a distance of 25 miles per day but rested on Sundays. Although they left Athens, Maine the year before and were heading west to Montana with the hope of making it to Oregon by winter, they admitted they would most likely not get past Colorado before stopping until spring.

Church said his method of transportation serves him well for attracting people and he takes advantage of the opportunity to preach about his faith.

"In our travels we have talked to all kinds of people, lawyers, doctors, priests, nuns and ministers as well as everyday people," he said.

Church's wife said she teaches Darlynn, 3, and Rolanda, 5, for two hours each day, "mostly from the Bible."

Special permission had been arranged for the wagon to cross the Big Mac that day, and the toll ...?

Well, they probably charged by the axle, as they normally do.

Over the years there have been some notable accidents that ranged from fender-benders to crashes of a serious nature that produced fatalities. While accidents like these happen all the time on large highways, the fact that they occurred on the Mackinac Bridge made them newsworthy.

The bridge's first-ever traffic fatality happened on July 22, 1966, when Russell McKeighan, 56, of Highland Park, Mich., remarked to his companion what a lovely view of the area they were enjoying, heading northbound near the center of the span.

He then slumped over, quick as that, dead of a heart attack.

A double-fatality occurred on Oct. 11, 1984 when the driver of a southbound Chevy Chevette – no doubt distracted by the view of the Straits and passing ships below – failed to see a Chevy Blazer in front of him that was disabled with a broken drive shaft. The driver plowed into the stopped car, and two passengers in the moving vehicle were killed.

The bridge's first traffic accident involved a trailer rollover on an icy November day in 1957.

Police, firemen and emergency personnel at the scene of a 1984 accident that killed two Michigan Technological University students. The Jaws of Life from the Mackinaw City Fire Department were used to cut the top off the Chevette and extricate the victims.

Ironically, the passengers – Michael Cardosi, 18, of Grosse Pointe Woods, Mich., and Gary Hubel, 20, of Warren, Mich. – were students at Michigan Technological University in Houghton, Mich., who had hitched a ride downstate and never made it home.

The Chevette's driver, Gregory Lang, 21, of Rochester, Mich., survived. The driver and sole occupant of the Blazer, Wade Mevnier, 23, of Windsor, Ont., was not injured in the accident.

A Canadian woman died and three other people were injured in a Sept. 3, 1988 collision on the bridge.

Constance Conway, 31, of Sault Ste. Marie, Ont., was traveling southbound on the inside steel-grated lane when she lost control and went over the median and struck a northbound vehicle, the St. Ignace Post of the Michigan State Police told the Cheboygan Daily Tribune.

Conway was taken to Mackinac Straits Hospital in St. Ignace and pronounced dead on arrival. A passenger, 20-year-old Henry Johnston, also of Sault Ste. Marie, was seriously injured and taken to Community Memorial Hospital in Cheboygan and later transferred to Northern Michigan Hospital in Petoskey.

Police reported that Johnston was wearing a seatbelt and that Conway was not.

The driver of the other vehicle, Russell Mieloszyk, 32, of Bessemer, Mich., and his passenger, Wanda Mieloszyk, also 32 and of Bessemer, were injured and taken to Mackinac Straits Hospital. Police said that both were wearing seatbelts.

On April 23, 1991, Arthur Brunelle of Marquette and his wife Dorothy, 67, were returning home from a Florida vacation when a bridge escort vehicle made a U-turn in front of them, hitting the Brunelle vehicle and sending it into the back of a parked semi-trailer truck. The bridge worker was turning north from the south-bound lanes to escort the waiting truck across the bridge and failed to see the Brunelle vehicle coming.

Dorothy Brunelle, who was not wearing a seat belt, died of her injuries less than two weeks after the accident. Arthur Brunelle, who was driving and wearing his seat belt, received only minor injuries. The driver of the bridge escort car was uninjured.

Escort vehicles routinely made U-turns at that location while using emergency lights, but discontinued the practice after the accident. They have utilized exit and entrance ramps there when picking up escorted vehicles ever since.

An illegal U-turn in the bridge's 50th anniversary year, 2007, seriously injured a Canadian couple when they attempted to cut across the highway on the bridge's south approach.

Alajos Kannar, of Manitouwadge, Ontario, was injured along with his wife when their vehicle was hit broadside while trying to cross the highway in a U-turn to reach a hotel.

"Kannar was northbound on I-75 just north of the Jamet Street on-ramp when he decided to attempt a U-turn to get to the Holiday Inn on the west side of the freeway," Mackinaw City Chief of Police Pat

This tractor-trailer was providing an escort and blocking wind for the small passenger car until it flipped over at Pier 17. The truck's trailer was empty - causing the problem.

Wyman said. "In doing so, Kannar's vehicle was hit broadside by another northbound vehicle, causing it to go into the southbound lane."

Mrs. Kannar was seriously injured in the Feb. 2 crash, while the other driver, Lee Avery of Crystal, Mich., was not injured.

A June 27, 1969 accident saw wind toss a camper trailer off a truck on the bridge, and almost took a car over the side with it.

Mr. and Mrs. Vernon Bowling of Ypsilanti told the Cheboygan Daily Tribune they were caught in a sudden storm while driving north on the bridge en route to Tahquamenon Falls. Bowling was driving when the couple left Mackinaw City in their convertible, but the rain had not yet started.

As they drove north, Mrs. Bowling said she saw a funnel cloud coming from the north side of the Straits.

"It seemed to be pulling the water up," she told the Tribune.

A Petoskey man driving a pick-up truck with a camper headed south had the camper blown off the truck as the winds hit. The camper flew across several lanes, hit the hood of the Bowling's convertible and dropped on the bridge ahead of them. The convertible and the trailer were pulled up so that the rear wheels were resting on the rail of the bridge. Mrs. Bowling said that the vehicles would rock up and down in the wind and she worried that the trailer would go over and pull the convertible with it, as the hitch held.

"My husband told me he prayed that the hitch would let loose," she said.

Bridge Authority workers arrived in minutes and cleared all vehicles from harm.

Vernon Bowling drove his damaged car on to a St. Ignace garage for repairs. While workmen were unfastening his trailer from the car, the trailer dropped on Bowling's foot, sending him to the hospital. His wife was treated for shock.

Another of the strangest accidents ever to occur on the bridge also took place in the 1960s, when a boat hit a car. Robert J. Brinker of St. Clair, Mich., had the boat and Oliver J. Craig of Britton, Mich., was driving the auto. The unusual collision took place when the boat blew off the top of Brinker's car and struck Craig's car in the opposite lane. No one was injured and damage was minor.

After hitting the auto, the aluminum boat

The steering on this piece of heavy equipment went awry, causing its big tires to nearly roll over the railing.

Work crews cleared the road deck and nobody was hurt.

bounced off the bridge deck and fell into the Straits. The Coast Guard searched for it for several hours without success.

Eight boats were blown off car tops in 1974 alone, for example. In 1973, lost boats were reported ten times. There were 11 in 1976. Residents along both peninsula shorelines are used to finding life jackets, coolers, caps and canoes on area beaches from vehicles that didn't have these items secured in the backs of pick-up trucks or inside boats being trailered across.

The year 1976 also saw 300 bales of hay spilled onto the bridge deck when a load became loose. The driver continued his crossing but didn't realize that his cargo of 80-pound bales of hay was dropping off his truck. A number of them fell off the bridge into the Straits.

Another time the Straits were white with milk when a tanker truck full of milk slid onto the guard rail, resting perilously on its side. When bridge workmen worried that the weight might cause it to shift over the edge, they drained the contents into the water. The lightened load allowed the trailer to be easily righted and the truck was able to drive on.

On Nov. 11, 1989, gusting winds apparently caused a pick-up truck to lose control, rolling the truck and sending part of the trailer behind it over the guardrail. Two days later the Mackinac Bridge Authority announced changes in signs, lighting and traffic control on the bridge.

Sometimes the long arm of the law reaches all the way to the Mackinac Bridge — and across it.

In 1997 a pick-up truck driven by two teenage detention center escapees rammed four police cars and smashed through the Big Mac's toll gates in a slow-speed chase that covered nearly 100 miles. The male suspects, 15 and 16, were caught after a short foot chase in St. Ignace, but it all began about 1 a.m. Aug. 24 near Gaylord when State Police tried to stop the truck for a broken headlight.

The truck mostly drove at 40 mph in leading police on the two-hour journey. Police from 10 jurisdictions dropped in and out of the chase as it continued along M-32, US 31 and finally onto I-75 across the Mackinac Bridge. The truck drove north on the wrong side of the bridge, rammed a State Police car and crashed through the toll gates, police said. In St. Ignace, the truck rammed three St. Ignace Police cars before the suspects fled on foot and were caught.

These accounts are by no means a complete listing of

In the early days of the operation of the bridge, many people clamored to be the first to cross in an unusual fashion. Most of these requests were denied for safety reasons.

all the accidents that have taken place on the Mackinac Bridge, but represent the major ones and illustrate the types of calls police and Bridge Authority workers have responded to over the past 50 years.

A ratio of better than 99.9999 percent of the vehicles that pass through the toll gates at Mackinac have a successful, uneventful crossing. Over the years the Authority has kept a diligent count of the number of crossings recorded each day, each month and each year.

It was a big deal when the one-millionth car crossed the bridge, and a bigger deal when the five-millionth crossing was recorded.

In 1982, the Mackinac Bridge celebrated its 25th Anniversary, and a Tawas City couple tried to time their crossing to coincide with the exact time – 2 p.m. on Nov.

1 – that the bridge had opened to traffic 25 years before.

The plan worked, and Charles and Gloria Danforth were stopped and congratulated by former Gov. G. Mennen Williams and a welcoming party. For the record, the Danforths were the 45,354,017th vehicle to cross in 25 years.

Of course, Williams had been the first, officially, on Nov. 1, 1957.

As the numbers grew, Bridge Authority personnel had the routine down to a science when they knew they were expecting a milestone crossing. The Bridge Authority administrator would plan for days in advance, counting the daily totals and predicting when the next milestone crossing would occur. There were small ceremonies to award milestone motorists prizes

The one-millionth vehicle to cross the Mackinac Bridge arrives northbound at the tollbooths.

This happy family became the two millionth crossing on a sunny summer day.

Larry Rubin presented a framed photo when these men became the three millionth crossing.

Being selected as the five-millionth crossing delighted this family — look at the smile on the youngster's face.

Mike McKillop of Gaylord crossed at 10:12 p.m. on Sept. 25, 1984 to become the 50 millionth bridge fare to cross the Mackinac Bridge. Administrator Walter North watched McKillop's 1983 Olds Cutlass drive up and presented him with dinners for two and a night's lodging in St. Ignace and Mackinaw City, courtesy of each city's tourist association.

from local merchants. A photo was usually taken and it was fun to watch the winners who were stopped at the tollbooths for they had no idea what was happening.

The ceremonial crossings took place in all sorts of weather and at all times of the day and night.

These events took place over the years until the day came when the Mackinac Bridge had a really big number to celebrate – 100 million vehicles.

On June 25, 1998, Dan Gilment of Alpena crossed the bridge on his motorcycle headed north from Alpena bound for a vacation in Eagle River, Wis. His friend, Jim Smith, was riding right behind him.

The date was Gilment's birthday, but as he approached the tollbooth at 5:15 p.m. on his 1981 Harley Davidson he was stunned to see balloons let loose into the sky and hear a fog horn sound as a crowd cheered his arrival.

Gilment had become the 100 millionth driver of a motor vehicle to cross the Mackinac Bridge since the span opened for operations Nov. 1, 1957.

"I don't know what to say," Gilment told the waiting reception committee at first. "Thank you very much. I feel fortunate."

Mackinac Bridge Administrator Hank Lotoszinski

Hank Lotoszinski of the Mackinac Bridge Authority was on hand along with many other well-wishers to greet Dan Gilment when he rode his 1981 Harley Davidson through the bridge toll booths. Gilment, of Alpena, became the 100 millionth bridge fare at 5:15 p.m. on June 25, 1998.

informed Gilment of his honor and Bridge Authority personnel and local area chambers of commerce showered the traveler with gifts. He received everything from T-shirts and fudge to a week of free motel rooms in the Upper Peninsula.

Gilment's friend was not dismayed that he had not won the honor.

"Just the luck of the draw, I guess," Smith said. "I'm happy for him."

The countdown to the 100 millionth vehicle started six months before the big day arrived, with analysts counting normal traffic totals of 15,000 to 20,000 vehicles per day at that time of the year, late June. The Bridge Authority uses an electronic counting procedure to keep track of vehicle crossings.

"We would know when we had 500 vehicles to go, 100 to go and so on, then we'd close down to one lane and identify the vehicle as it came through," said former Bridge Administrator Walter North.

Before continuing on with his trip, Gilment informed the well-wishers that he would be getting married in three weeks.

Speaking of weddings, two couples received permission to get married on the bridge one year and the ceremony took place on Pier 22, the north anchor block.

"The ceremonies were conducted by the mayor," recalled Larry Rubin, former Bridge Authority executive. "All went well until it was over and the happy couples jumped in their cars and left without tipping the mayor. He wasn't happy about it."

This U.S. Army tank may qualify as one of the heaviest vehicles, pound-for-pound, that has crossed the Mighty Mac.

The weather didn't cooperate but the elephants did when a circus staged performances in the area that later became Bridge View Park. The trainers walked the four pachyderms out for the photo.

Mackinac Bridge Authority Administrator Walter North, at left, thought he'd seen everything until he got a call that there was a deer loose on the bridge. Motorists gawked and some petted and fed the docile animal until it could be guided back to the mainland.

7
Tollbooth Tales

There are many jobs to be done to keep the Mackinac Bridge operating smoothly, but as long as it costs money to cross it there will always be a need for toll collectors to accept cash, tokens and fare cards and perform any number of extra tasks that must be carried out on a daily basis.

Collecting money is the obvious job of the toll collector, and at first glance most people probably think that it would be the most boring job in the world.

At times, it can be.

But anyone who has stayed with the job for more than one summer's worth of employment will tell you that "minding the Mac" has its moments of excitement, comedy, frustration and gratification. Sometimes they all occur on the same shift, but working as a Mackinac Bridge toll collector gives you a unique "window on the world" that keeps you in touch with what is happening all around the area, the state and even the nation.

Maybe all around the world.

Most collectors will tell you that they didn't work for very long before they had someone drive up who claimed they didn't have the money to pay the fare.

"We've had guys who have told the toll collector that they had just been robbed," said Larry Rubin, executive secretary of the Mackinac Bridge Authority

for many years. "Lots of truck drivers, especially those from the south, plead that they have no money until they deliver their load of melons or oranges or whatever they're carrying.

"Some women will just give the collector a sweet smile and say they're broke, hoping he'll let them across without paying," Rubin told the Lansing State Journal. "Everybody pays – one vehicle, one fare, no exceptions."

Toll collectors were told in the early years of the bridge's operation that missed tolls would be deduct-

Operations Supervisor Ben Wiggins (left), checks fare reports with toll collectors Ray Kaminsky (center) and Glenn Gustafson (right). A coat, tie and cap was the uniform of the day in the early years of the bridge's operation.

ed from their paychecks.

"It's surprising how many people can dig in their pocket or glove compartment and somehow 'find' the money, once they're confronted by a non-budging toll collector," Rubin said.

At one time the Authority did allow collectors to "loan" toll fees to patrons and retain an article of value which was returned when the fee was paid. But the collector still had to account for the toll when turning in the receipts from each shift.

"We had an unofficial policy then," veteran Bridge Administrator Walter North said, referring to the era prior to the 1970s, "and it was up to the fare supervisor, that they would take something of value in return for paying the toll out of their own pocket. There would be an incentive for that person to return and repay the collector. We would take 8-track tapes, spare tires, watches. It decreased when the tolls dropped to $1.50. By then people who thought they didn't have enough money to cross would find that much in change under their car seat or money somewhere they didn't think they had."

"We allowed this on a limited basis but didn't want it to get out of hand," Rubin explained. "We

couldn't afford to get into the hock shop business."

He said a "sad-story kitty" was once accumulated, with each staff member tossing in $5, the idea being that the fund would take care of extreme hardship cases.

"But the collectors suddenly got softer when it wasn't their money they were loaning," Rubin said, "and the kitty didn't last three months."

Former Supervisor Clyde O'Rourke got to the point where he no longer would take collateral items in the 1960s but simply trusted people to send him the

This fare schedule was in effect when the bridge opened in 1957. It soon increased to $3.50 for a passenger car and then to $3.75 before dropping years later.

The toll plaza was a stark, lonely outpost when it first opened in 1957, especially at night.

money he put in when they didn't have enough.

He said most did.

"Once in awhile we got burned," Rubin added. "We had a supervisor, George Malner – a former Michigan State Trooper – who loaned a guy money enough for the toll after questioning him for quite awhile. He took a spare tire as a guarantee. Later the State Police informed us that the car was stolen, so poor George was out both his money and the tire. We all had a good laugh over that one, including George."

Once a man came through from Columbus, Ohio driving a Cadillac and said the only way he could pay was to cash a check. The Mackinac Bridge Authority does not accept checks for single-fare tolls, but this was in the old days and somebody was tempted to bend the rule this one time.

"He was a nice looking guy," remembered Henry Devereaux, a long-time employee who started when the bridge opened in 1957, "about 55. He had credit cards galore, a letter authorizing him to drive the car and another letter that said he was going to open up a printing shop somewhere in the U.P. He just didn't have any cash. We cashed the check for the toll and the next day the State Police picked him up in Escanaba. It turned out he had escaped from an Ohio mental hospital."

Then there was the man who dropped his wallet containing $300 in cash on the plaza. He came back the next day and found it, laying untouched in the snow.

"There was another guy who phoned me one Sunday morning in 1958 and said he'd left his wallet in the phone booth at the toll plaza," Devereaux said.

"He told me there was five or six hundred in it. I rescued it and a few hours later this gent shows up and identifies himself. He was in dirty overalls and was wearing a cheap cap. He offered me five bucks reward because I'd saved him the trouble of sending

to his office for money.

"I turned down his tip, because he looked so hard up," Devereaux added. "He left the office and I followed him out. There he was, climbing into a brand new Cadillac. And his wife was wearing the most beautiful mink coat I guess ever crossed the bridge."

For years, the Salvation Army would help out people who had no money to cross and appeared to need more help than just the bridge toll. In recent times, fare collectors have offered cashless motorists directions on how to find the closest ATM at a local bank.

Perhaps it's the idea that most motorists who cross the five-mile span have just completed a drive of considerable distance – whether they are arriving from the north or the south. Add to that the fact that many who cross the bridge are doing so for the first time, and are likely quite unfamiliar with the Straits of Mackinac area or Northern Michigan in general.

But, people being people, motorists say the darndest things to toll collectors and ask questions that may have to be heard to be believed.

A popular quip among area workers is to tell the story of the tourist who asked them, "What time does the bridge swing over to Mackinac Island?" Believe it

Mary Otto of Cheboygan was the first female toll collector hired to work at the bridge.

or not, that question does get asked sometimes.

Of course, Mackinac Island is only served by ferryboats and by air, and the bridge connects the upper and lower peninsulas of Michigan. It doesn't change destinations.

Yet other questions asked of toll collectors can many times rival the "swinging bridge" query for originality, banality and sheer absurdity.

There are questions about the remoteness of the area:

"Are there any restaurants up here?"

"Do you need to see my passport?"

"How far can I drive up here?"

"Is it always foggy here?"

"Is this still Michigan or did we cross over?"

"If I go up and around, will I end up over there?"

"What time do you close?"

There are questions about the lakes:

"What part of the Great Lakes do you get smoked fish?"

"Are we on the island now?"

"What lake am I driving over?"

"What river did I just cross?"

"How is Lake Huron and Lake Michigan connected?"

There are questions about paying the toll, which in 2007 was $2.50 for a two-axle car or truck, each way:

"All I have is a hundred dollar bill, but I have the 50 cents."

"Can you break a $10 bill?"

"Is the Upper Peninsula lane cheaper?"

"You guys must have gotten a big raise, huh?"

"Keep the change."

"This is the first time I've been up here since they put in the toll booths."

The tollbooths have always been here.

And then there are questions or comments from those who try to get out of paying the fare altogether:

"I already paid the state enough. I don't want to pay."

"I just got on in Mackinaw City. Is it still $2.50?"

"You have to pay both ways now?"

"I remember when the toll was only 75 cents."

"We're with Girl Scout Troop 745 and we're just staying in Mackinaw City. Do we still have to pay?"

Of course, the bridge toll has never been less than $1.50 and has always been charged both directions.

Sometimes people crossing the bridge assume that toll collectors know just about everything about faraway places, including the weather:

"Is it snowing in Marquette?"

"Have any tornadoes touched down in Bay City?"

"Does this fog go all the way?"

They test local knowledge about the obvious:

"How long is the bridge? Five miles? Is that from here to there?"

"Which direction is West US 2?"

"Which one is Exit 344A?"

"Where do I pick up I-75?"

Motorists are already on I-75.

Some get personal with the toll collectors:

"What's up Bridge Lady?"

"Man…you look just like Jackie Chan!"

"Hey baby, why don't you just hop in and head south with me?"

"Look kids – a real Indian!"

"Do you wanna ride across the bridge with me?"

The tollbooths were built to handle traffic on either side to accommodate both directions if necessary.

And sometimes they get ridiculous:

"Is there a net under the bridge?"
"What are the life rings for?"
"Is it against the law to fish off the bridge?"
"Have you seen a red truck hauling a boat?"
"How big is the parking lot on Mackinac Island? There is none? Then where am I going to park my car?"

Through it all, the staff of the Mackinac Bridge Authority handles the constant dialogue with grace and dignity. Thousands of motorists daily ask for and receive answers as to mileage to various destinations, current bridge conditions, and basic directions to attractions, dining and lodging facilities. Many times travelers pass on comments about the highway driving they've just seen, with details of accidents, weather or detours. The bridge employees relay these with a smile when asked.

When the Mackinac Bridge Authority elected to install token lanes and machines to accept them and fare cards, some collectors feared it meant the eventual end of their jobs. However, many locals who use the alternative payment methods use the automatic lanes when in a hurry – for there are usually very small lines – but otherwise hand the token or fare card to a toll collector to also say hello or request or pass along information.

Some travelers who have come a long way seem to want someone to talk to, and look at the tollbooth stop as a sort of rest stop or break from the highway miles. There are convenient rest areas on both sides of the highway adjacent to the tollbooths for this purpose, but some drivers just seem to want to chat.

Occasionally, it turns into more than that.

A 41 year-old Jackson, Mich., man who chucked a hockey puck at a Mackinac Bridge tollbooth attendant found himself in a whole lot more trouble than just not paying the $1.50 toll.

Kenneth Howard Wilcox flipped the puck at fare collector Tracey Campbell of Mackinaw City just before 5 a.m. August 28, 2001 and kept driving.

Wilcox then led Cheboygan County Sheriff's Deputies, Michigan State Police Troopers and Mackinaw City Police waiting for him on the south end of the bridge on a 15-mile chase down I-75 that reached 90 mph before police stopped his car near the Levering Road exit.

"When apprehended, he had a large butcher knife in his hand," Deputy Larry Sproul told the Cheboygan Daily Tribune. "He reached for his glove box but gave the knife up and was taken into custody without a struggle."

Police then determined that Wilcox was intoxicated. A further search of the vehicle revealed a stash of marijuana.

Wilcox was sentenced in Cheboygan 53rd Circuit Court to nine months in jail for carrying a concealed weapon. He lost his car for 60 days on a charge of operating under the influence of liquor and was

The automatic commuter lane speeds up fare collections from motorists who use tokens or fare cards.

ordered to pay $150 to the Cheboygan County Sheriff's Department.

He was also fined $100 for possessing marijuana.

Finally, Wilcox was placed on probation for two years and ordered to pay an $2,430 in additional fines and probation supervision fees.

And to think that all he had to do was find $1.50 or ask the toll collector for help.

One day a station wagon pulled up to the tollbooth and had a full-sized lion in the back. The toll collectors on duty surely stared at that sight.

Before signage was replaced to clarify the St. Ignace interchange with I-75 and US 2, motorists sometimes mistakenly got back on the same highway in the opposite direction and crossed the bridge again. Plenty of requests to make U-turns were made by those who caught their mistake as they approached the tollbooths.

A Canadian trucker headed for Winnipeg kept crossing the bridge again and again until he said to an attendant, "How many bridges you got like this?" He had already paid more than $30 in tolls, in the days when it didn't cost as much as it does today.

It isn't always Canadians who get into the funniest jams.

But there's the story about the two Canadian couples traveling together and the wives were fast asleep in the back seat of the car under some blankets. The husbands stopped in Mackinaw City for gas, then went inside to get a cup of coffee for the road. The wives awoke and decided to run to the restrooms on the outside of the building. The men came out with their coffee, hopped in the car and drove across the bridge, assuming their wives were still asleep in the back seat. The guys were plenty surprised when a toll collector informed them that their wives had called and were still at the Mackinaw City gas station. The women were brought over in a bridge patrol car.

Another legendary story among fare collectors is the one about a motorist who crossed with a pick-up camper from the Mackinaw City side.

"The wind lifted the camper off his truck and deposited it on the bridge," Larry Rubin recalled for the Grand Rapids Press in 1972. "But he didn't discover it was missing until he stopped in Seney for lunch. That's about 80 miles from here.

"He back-tracked all the way here and found that our maintenance department had rescued the thing for him," Rubin added. "Boy, was his face red."

"You meet all kinds of people in this job, in all walks of life," said Devereaux. "Some are arrogant – like the law student who tried to argue that we had no right to collect the toll. Some are amusing. Some are destitute.

"You see strange things, like women who have taken off all their clothes on a hot day and just drive through, nonchalant as a nude baby. Most of the hardship cases seem to come at night."

A Plexiglas weather cover can be used to give fare collectors relief from cold winds at the Straits.

Another duty of toll collectors is to sometimes be on the lookout for a particular car or driver because of a request by the police. Sometimes it's due to a call from a family. As an example, in 1979 the Mackinac Bridge Authority delivered 212 emergency messages to motorists via the toll collectors.

Most toll supervisors agree that of all the odd happenings that take place on the Mackinac Bridge, the strangest occurs every year during firearm deer hunting season.

"We are plagued with phone calls from wives asking us to tell their deer-hunting husbands that they've left their rifles at home by the front door," Rubin says.

Toll collectors spend their entire shift making change. On July 1, 1964 there was a race to the Mackinac Bridge, but it wasn't a bicycle competition. It was a frantic trip to bring spare change to the toll-takers at the Mighty Mac.

A pile of 4,000 quarters was rushed to the bridge that day to ease a coin shortage bottleneck. A relay of State Police cars ferried the coins to the Straits. Bridge Comptroller Richard E. Davies had reported that banks in several states were unable to answer his appeal for quarters to make change for motorists in bridge crossings. Grand Rapids City Treasurer Robert Sterkenburg heard of the problem and came to the rescue. He took quarters collected from parking meters and swapped the quarters for a $1,000 check from the bridge office.

The Mackinac Bridge is unusual among toll bridges in North America in that the fare must be paid by motorists traveling in each direction. Most other bridges charge a larger fare but in only one direction.

In 1999, the Bridge Authority and the Michigan Department of Transportation looked at the prospect of instituting a one-way toll. Three public hearings were held to release the study results. The sessions were held in Mackinaw City, St. Ignace and Lansing.

"The study looked at several areas of the Mackinac Bridge and its operations to determine whether one-way tolls are viable from an operational standpoint," said State Transportation Director James R. DeSana. "We want to be able to discuss this report with the public, both in the Straits area and in our state capital, and hear our customers' perspectives on one-way tolls."

The study looked at three major areas for which the conversion of one-way tolls were evaluated – revenue impacts, including potential traffic diversion from doubling of tolls in one direction; operating and physical requirements, such as toll plaza modifications, speed control, facility accessibility and truck weighing/inspection; and financial impacts, that is, operating and capital costs. One-way tolls have been implemented in various bridge locations in the country, with some savings in operating costs.

"We are pleased to host these public hearings on

Aggie O'Brien collects fares, makes change, gives directions, forecasts the weather and much more during a typical eight-hour shift at the Mackinac Bridge tollbooth.

the important topic of one-way tolls," said MBA Executive Secretary Hank Lotoszinski. "We expect to share findings from the study, learn the public's interest in one-way tolls and come away with a solid customer perception."

The final report of the study was prepared by Vollmer Associates.

No matter what the rest of the country thought, two-way tolls were determined to be the best solution at Mackinac. For one thing, there was a perception that the tolls would be collected heading north, which led to a second perception that motorists would have to "pay to get to the U.P." This thought, many believed, would discourage tourism.

Another factor was that – even though crossers currently had to pay in both directions – a higher fare in one direction only would further discourage travel to the north.

The fare system was left as it was, paying in both directions.

In 1998 fare revenues totaled $10.6 million with more than 4.8 million vehicles crossing the bridge.

When customers pay, they mostly use cash or coins.

But frequent crossers were given new options when the paper coupon, or "scrip" system was phased out in favor of bridge token coins in 2002.

Motorists could purchase commuter coins in packs of 24 for $30 or a commuter card for the same price (raised to 24 crossings for $36 in 2003). The new gold-colored coins (tokens) and the commuter cards can be used in the two automatic coin-machine lanes, or in the regular tollbooths.

"The idea to use tokens actually came from our customers," said Authority Chairman Murray D. Wikol. "This is a great opportunity to produce a com-

Operations Manager Dean Steiner displays old scrip tickets used before tokens were sold.

The first scrip tickets were worth one dollar.

The later version covered any two-axle passenger vehicle.

memorative coin as well as provide another quick payment option for our regular customers."

The first commemorative coin had a picture of the Mackinac Bridge on one side and "Michigan's #1 Civil Engineering Project of the 20th Century" on the other. It commemorates the selection of the Mackinac Bridge by the Michigan Chapter of the American Society of Civil Engineers.

Commuter scrip sales ceased on April 1, 2002. Those in circulation were said to be accepted in the tollbooths until Dec., 31, 2002. Commuter cards were available at the same discounted fare of $1.25 per trip for passenger vehicles, and later increased to $1.50 when the fares went up. Customers can deposit funds into their commuter card accounts in increments of $30.

Commercial scrip sales were also due to be discontinued on April 1 that year. They were replaced with commercial debit cards.

"We've completed the testing phase of our new debit card programs and we're ready to roll them out to all of our customers," Bridge Authority Executive Secretary Henry A. Lotoszinski said then. "Our trucking customers have been very pleased with the many features of the debit card program."

But on Sept. 17, 2003 the Mackinac Bridge Authority announced it would accept paper scrip, used as payment for bridge tolls, through Dec. 31, 2003. It turned out that there were a lot more scrip coupons still in the paying customers' hands than previously thought, and they needed more time to use them up or turn them in for token coins. Paper scrip was officially no longer accepted by the tollbooths beginning January 2004.

The Authority also announced changes in Canadian currency and coin transactions. Effective April 1, 2002, transactions must be all U.S. or all Canadian when transacting at the tollbooths. Mixing of currencies was no longer allowed. The currency exchange rate in 2002 was 50 percent, but varies greatly with economic trends.

Tolls were eventually increased in 2003 to $2.50 for a passenger car and $3 per axle for commercial motorcoaches. Other fares went up proportionately, but regular commuters still got a good deal at $1.50 per trip, as of 2003.

From time to time, new token designs were offered in commemoration of events or people to be honored within the history of transportation at the Straits.

These included a token coin to commemorate the Michigan Department of Transportation's 100th anniversary, introduced on June 30, 2005.

"From the days of the car ferries to the Mackinac Bridge, St. Ignace has been very important to transportation," stated Bridge Authority Administrator Bob Sweeney. "The new coin will be a favorite among collectors and commuters alike."

Another special ceremony was held June 16, 2006 commemorating the eight state-operated car ferries that helped millions of passengers cross the Straits of Mackinac prior to completion of the Mackinac Bridge in 1957. New coins were released that portrayed the vessels that did the job a different way than the bridge does today.

"For over 30 years, car ferries were the only effective way to cross the Straits of Mackinac," said MBA Board Chairman William Gnodtke. "In 1923, the Ariel was the first state-operated vessel to serve a key transportation role before the Mackinac Bridge was built."

"Whether it's a ferry, a road, or a bridge, transportation is the vital link that stimulates the economy in this great state," said State Transportation Director Kirk T. Steudle. "This year, we are dedicating and circulating the new coins as a way to recognize the historical significance of the ferry service."

Beginning in 1923, the following state-operated

vessels made their way across the Straits:

Ariel, 1923
Sainte Ignace, 1924
Mackinaw City, 1924
Straits of Mackinac, 1928
City of Cheboygan, 1937
City of Munising, 1938
City of Petoskey, 1940
Vacationland, 1952

NOTE: Two additional vessels were leased by the state from the Mackinaw Transportation Company.

"Mickey Sweeney, former Captain of the Vacationland (and my father), worked on all 10 of the ferries," stated MBA Administrator Bob Sweeney in 2006. "At the time it was in service, the Vacationland was a state-of-the-art vessel and often referred to as the, 'Queen of the Fleet.'"

The new car ferry coins were the sixth in a series of bridge toll coins, or tokens, which customers can use to cross the bridge. In 2006 eight sets were available, with plans for a new token coin honoring David B. Steinman to mark the 50th anniversary of the opening of the bridge.

In 2003, a local merchant jeopardized the token system by attempting to profit from it.

Under a new toll structure that took effect May 1, 2003, travelers in cars, vans and pick-up trucks with two axles are required to pay $2.50 each way to cross the bridge, up from $1.50

Commuters can still buy tokens for $1.50 each.

The Mackinac Bridge Authority offers commuter cards with 24 passes – or a roll of 24 tokens – for $36, giving commuters a 40 percent savings off the standard passenger vehicle fare.

A Mackinaw City gasoline station tried buying tokens for $1.50 and then re-selling them to northbound travelers for $2. The deal saved the traveler 50 cents and netted the gas station a 50 cent profit.

"We're actually dismayed by it, to think that someone would take advantage of the situation and sell the tokens for less," William H. Gnodtke, chairman of the Authority, told the St. Ignace News. "That's less money that can be used for bridge maintenance projects."

"This is putting the whole commuter program in jeopardy," Bridge Administrator Bob Sweeney was quoted by the Cheboygan Daily Tribune. "The commuter tokens are strictly for those who frequently cross the bridge; mostly they are local residents."

The Authority now would only sell a commuter card — not tokens — to someone suspected of conducting a similar scam today.

Despite the many conveniences offered to customers for paying tolls on the bridge, about 30 people attempt to avoid paying the bridge toll each year, costing the Mackinac Bridge Authority less than $100 annually. However, the issue is more serious than chasing a $2.50 fare.

Skipping through the tollbooth without paying on the Mackinac Bridge has meant a maximum $500 fine and 30 days in jail due to a bill signed in 2005 by Michigan Gov. Jennifer Granholm.

"The problem arises because those who do skip through are often driving drunk or carrying illegal drugs," said Rep. Scott Shackleton, R-Sault Ste. Marie.

"They can claim they were stopped illegally when a police officer pulls them over for running the bridge. This law will help police ensure that somebody trying to slip by the tollbooths can't use that defense."

There previously had been no penalty for scofflaws who avoided paying the toll. House Bill 5801 changed that when it went into effect.

Michigan's Civil Engineering Project of the 20th Century

Bridge View Park
June 12, 2002
Dedication

Prentiss M. Brown
*Father of the
Mackinac Bridge*

May 30th
2003

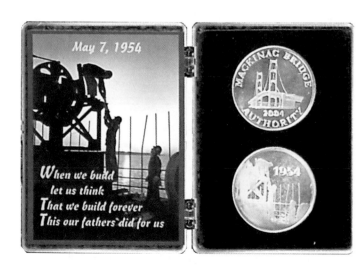

May 7, 1954

*When we build
let us think
That we build forever
This our fathers did for us*

Michigan Department of Transportation

Celebrates
100 Years
1905 - 2005
OF TRANSPORTATION

Mackinac Bridge fare collectors verify that a full moon brings out unusual customers through the tollbooths. All are greeted with a smile, for they keep the job interesting.

Maintenance of the Mac

The maintenance of the Mackinac Bridge involves work of all types. There is painting, electrical, steel and iron repair, welding and cement work done on the bridge itself, and plowing, sanding, washing and occasional patching of the roadway on the bridge.

Contractors come in to do the heavy-duty painting, paving and electrical jobs, but much work of that sort is also performed by the local crew that staffs the Mackinac Bridge Authority's Maintenance Department.

To work on the bridge, cross it or simply view its magnificent length, it helps to understand a little bit about the span to put it in perspective. It's a suspension bridge, and there are many similar designs in the world. Only two are bigger.

Two towers, 552 feet tall, hold up 42,000 miles of cable strung between two giant concrete anchor blocks that hold it all in place. The cable is concentrated into two 24 1/4 - inch diameter cores wrapped inside a protective coating of pipe.

The suspension holds up the roadway, and Dr. Steinman designed the whole structure to withstand 2 1/2 times all the recorded natural stresses of weather in the area plus four times the anticipated load of vehicles crossing the bridge.

The bridge flexes to accommodate weather

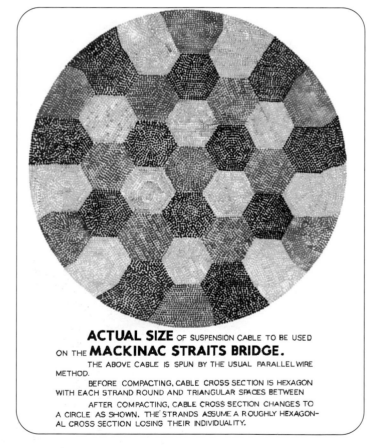

ACTUAL SIZE OF SUSPENSION CABLE TO BE USED ON THE **MACKINAC STRAITS BRIDGE.**
    THE ABOVE CABLE IS SPUN BY THE USUAL PARALLEL WIRE METHOD.
    BEFORE COMPACTING, CABLE CROSS SECTION IS HEXAGON WITH EACH STRAND ROUND AND TRIANGULAR SPACES BETWEEN
    AFTER COMPACTING, CABLE CROSS SECTION CHANGES TO A CIRCLE AS SHOWN. THE STRANDS ASSUME A ROUGHLY HEXAGONAL CROSS SECTION LOSING THEIR INDIVIDUALITY.

This sign was produced to show the arrangement within the main suspension cable on the Mackinac Bridge. The individual cable strands are about the size of a pencil in diameter. The full-size sign showed the compacted cable diameter at 24 1/4 inches.

stress or vehicle weight.

There are two large finger joints at the towers to accommodate all the expansion of the suspended spans. There are 11 smaller finger joints and five sliding joints across the Mackinac Bridge. In addition, there are 13 expansion joints for the south viaduct spans – one for each of these simple spans. This adds up to a total of 31 total joints.

All suspension bridges are designed to move to accommodate wind, changes in temperature and weight. It is possible that the deck at center span could move as much as 35 feet (east or west) due to high winds. This would only happen under severe wind conditions. The deck would not swing or "sway" but rather inch slowly in one direction based on the force and direction of the wind. After the wind subsides, the weight of the vehicles crossing would slowly move it back into center position. This could take days.

Sometimes, during extreme wind conditions, locals will drive down to the shore to look at the waves and the bridge. At times it appears that the suspended portion in the middle has "blown out" and looks somewhat flexed to one side, usually to the east.

The bridge can raise or lower as much as 10 feet, varying with the air temperature. The tops of the tow-

ers also have the ability to flex inward 10 to 15 feet, depending on the traffic load. These movements are practically invisible to the naked eye.

The steel superstructure will support one ton per lineal foot per roadway (northbound or southbound). The length of the steel superstructure is 19,243 feet. Each direction will, therefore, support 19,243 tons. The total weight supported could be 38,486 tons (2 x 19,243 tons). The bridge could hold loaded semi-trailer trucks from St. Ignace to Mackinaw City and back again, and in the time it would take to get that load onto the bridge it would slowly flex to absorb the weight. It would then gradually return to normal after the load was released.

The width of the roadway is 54 feet. The outside lanes are 12 feet wide (2), the inside lanes are 11 feet wide (2), the center mall is two feet wide, and the catwalk, curb and rail width is three feet on each side - totaling 54 feet. The stiffening truss width in the suspended span is 68 feet wide, making it wider than the roadway it supports.

The height of the roadway at mid-span is approximately 200 feet above water level. The vertical clearance at normal temperature is 155 feet at the center of the main suspension span and 135 feet at the boundaries of the 3,000 ft. navigation channel.

Expansion joints allow the bridge to flex when necessary. The span can become as much as 28 feet longer than normal under a heavy load.

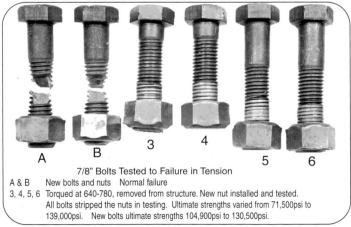

7/8" Bolts Tested to Failure in Tension
A & B   New bolts and nuts   Normal failure
3, 4, 5, 6   Torqued at 640-780, removed from structure. New nut installed and tested.
All bolts stripped the nuts in testing.   Ultimate strengths varied from 71,500psi to 139,000psi.   New bolts ultimate strengths 104,900psi to 130,500psi.

Bolt testing was conducted to ensure strength at high stress levels.

The inside lanes of the suspended portion of the bridge are made of steel grating. It's lighter than concrete, and helps reduce the load borne by the suspension cables. In addition, air can flow through the grating, rain can drip through it and snow can even be plowed down through it or over the sides of the bridge. Looking up from the water, vehicles appear to be crossing the bridge in mid-air on the grated lanes. They, too, must be repaired and replaced when necessary.

When the Mackinac Bridge was first completed in 1957, it had a "red lead" primer color. The Big Mac didn't get its green and ivory color until the next year.

Every summer, some portion of the bridge undergoes a sandblasting and painting process that has been a never-ending job for more than 50 years. Weather permitting, the Mac is paintable if it is warmer than 40 degrees with low humidity and wind velocities are within safety margins to have workmen on the bridge.

In another era without OSHA regulations, EPA and DEQ controls, painting the bridge was done in a very different manner than it is today.

Even the paint was different.

At the turn of the century, 2000, engineers realized that all the sanding and painting of so many years had built up a coat of paint that was about six layers thick. The added weight of all that paint was making the bridge heavier than it needed to be.

Another problem was the paint itself, a lead-based formula that didn't pass today's standards.

The process was begun to sandblast the entire bridge – from south to north – and remove all the lead-based paint. This is done under a canvas tent that keeps all contaminants contained where a giant vacuum is operated from the bridge's road deck to draw paint chips, toxic fumes and excess paint spray into a tanker truck parked above.

The bare metal is inspected for signs of wear or rust and treated.

Then a newer, safer, zinc-oxide paint mix is applied with a spraying system that does a faster, more complete job than the old brush and can method – still used where needed.

The process of working the entire bridge free of the lead-based paint takes many years, far more than the usual process of painting the bridge on a seasonal schedule of routine maintenance.

In the 1980s, for example, it was estimated that it took 40,000 gallons of paint and eight summers to finish the bridge from one end to the other. Then they would start over again.

Today, the process takes about a year less, but with other needed maintenance chores being done the Mac isn't painted as continuously as it once was. Other work must be done first.

Painters on the bridge wear protective gear to keep paint off skin.

Cable painters are hoisted hundreds of feet into the air to do their work. They brave weather elements on a daily basis.

Mackinac Bridge workers Dick Campbell (right), Fred Scott (left), and Elmer Gust (above) apply bridge paint the old-fashioned way with a brush and can. It took eight years to paint the bridge using this method each summer.

William Bellant was just out of the Navy and a Cheboygan resident in his early 20s when he took a job painting the Mackinac Bridge for three years in the late 1950s, applying the first coats of green paint.

He recalls being paid $4.35 an hour to work more than 500 feet above the Straits of Mackinac. Some weeks, painting could only be done three days out of seven because of the weather, Bellant remembered.

He said that one day, a crane broke and a 25-gallon drum of paint fell into the water, creating a bright green streak.

"On the weekend, we went down to Rogers City and found where it had finally come ashore," Bellant told the Associated Press in 1982. "There was a two-mile stretch of green shoreline. Every rock had a green mark on it."

Not all of the paint that fell from the bridge did so by accident, Bellant added.

"We were painting on the deck – out near the middle – and a 19 year-old kid on our crew decided to have some fun as a U.S. Steel ore carrier passed underneath us," he revealed. "So he let go with a five-gallon paint can that he had just opened.

"The paint hit on the deck near the bow of the ship and made a splat 15 feet or so across," Bellant continued. "The sailors scattered like a bunch of ants. It was funny except that the bucket nearly hit one of the crewmen. The next day, there was quite an inquisition – we didn't squeal."

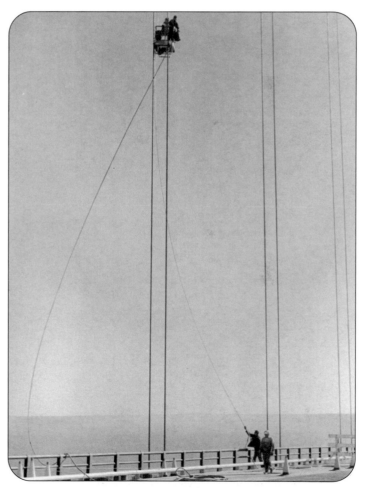

Hoisting a man aloft in a 55-gallon barrel for cable painting or maintenance was common practice under work standards of years ago. Today the work is done using OSHA-approved lift equipment complete with safety harness. It's still not for the faint of heart.

In the spring of 1958, workmen began changing the color of the Mackinac Bridge towers from "red lead" to ivory. In the lower two photos, the access hatches to the first and and second levels above the roadway are visible.

William Bellant's recollection of his work days on the bridge includes the unspoken rule that the painters ignored daily orders to "tie in" – attach themselves to safety rope lines while working.

"It was understood that if they caught you using a safety belt, you were fired on the spot," Bellant said. "It took too much time to tie and untie it. All the instructions were just to justify the insurance company."

Without a doubt the complete reverse of upholding the policy would be in effect today.

During inclement weather, the Authority's paint crew will sometimes paint the inside of the two giant towers – an extremely difficult and uncomfortable duty. Progress is very slow, however it is a very low-priority chore.

There's also a total of 6,800 feet of guardrail that has to be sandblasted, primed and given three coats of paint. The north and south approach viaducts also require spot blasting, priming and finish coating.

These before and after photos of the Mackinac Bridge's color scheme show the original construction color - "red lead" - and the finished product of green and ivory.

Today, sandblasting and painting the Mackinac Bridge is done inside canvas work areas to satisfy environmental requirements. Vacuum trucks suction out all contaminants so that no paint, sandblasting materials or paint chips get into the water or the air at the Straits of Mackinac.

Every summer, engineers from the offices of Steinman, Boynton, Gronquist & Birdsall of New York City, the Authority's consultants, made a minute inspection of the bridge as required under terms of the Authority's contract with the bond-holders. Their consultations continue today and the firm constantly remarks about how well the Big Mac is maintained compared with other bridges they visit.

Sometimes maintenance work on the bridge

An ingenious traveler system is lifted into place, allowing workmen to access the underside of the bridge and work within the box beams for painting, maintenance and security matters.

The motorized travelers can move under the length of the entire suspended portion of the span.

Suspension cables are inspected using a series of "picks" that separate the cable bands and allow for a peek inside.

involves more than routine shop work or repairs.

In 1997 five bridge workers were involved in a rescue mission that will long be remembered. On July 24, a raccoon was discovered on a concrete ledge of an anchor block, 110 feet below the nearest horizontal surface and within 10 feet of sheer vertical concrete above the water line.

Originally, workman Al Stempki called the DNR. An officer in Newberry informed him that he was within the law to destroy the animal.

However, Stempki, Bob Cena, Mark Kinjorski, Dave White, Tom Hillock and Joel Methner launched the 40-foot bridge patrol boat and attempted a rescue.

The raccoon seemed less interested in the rescue than the bridge workers, Stempki told the Cheboygan Daily Tribune.

"He was feisty," Stempki said. "If he was injured, it sure didn't show. We had to tap him on the rear with a pole to get him to fall into a bucket. He fought us every step of the way."

The raccoon was safely turned over to Robert Roback, Mackinac County Animal Control officer, who promised to release it into the woods.

How the raccoon arrived at the base of the anchor pier remains a mystery of the bridge.

Over the years, fiber-optic cable, new electric wiring, replacement lighting, new steel grating panels and other equipment have been added to the Mackinac Bridge. It's as though any part that could possibly wear out is on a schedule for replacement. The roadway bed of the bridge is set

Paul White returns the bridge boat to the dock with a passenger - a raccoon found on the ledge of an anchor block.

A fiber-optic cable installation was underway on the bridge in June of 2001.

for replacement in the year 2017, a massive project. The light bulbs and globes have to be changed on the cables and atop the towers, a job done by workmen who walk up the cables – safety-harnessed, of course – and switch bulbs just as you do in your kitchen at home. However, bridge workers can have a drop of more than 550 feet below them, with a water depth of nearly 300 feet at center span.

The bridge cable lighting originally had a color scheme of all amber globes. That has varied over the years to a red, blue and green combination at Christmas to a patriotic red, white and blue in the summer for the 4th of July.

Maintenance work atop the towers and at several stages above and below the roadway are accessed by tower elevators – one to each tower. A locked hatchway at roadway level must be opened to gain entry. The elevator will hold two and one-half to three people, workmen joke, depending on their size. The elevator will rise at a rate of about 100 feet per minute, making a ride to the top a bit of a journey. Upon exiting the hatch at the top floor,

visitors must scramble through a honeycombed network of steel girders and beams before finding a steel-runged ladder that juts out of the tower wall.

It's a direct vertical climb of about 30 feet – straight up – to another hatchway which opens to the walkway atop the tower and the most magnificent view imaginable. It's usually breezy enough to make it uncomfortable to have a hat or sunglasses

Both towers can be accessed by elevators from bottom to top.

The wind gauges at center span are calibrated for accuracy.

The bridge received an electrical upgrade in the summer of 2000.

Changing light bulbs must be done on roadway lights…

… and up on the suspension cables, as demonstrated by bridge electrician Melvin LaChapelle …

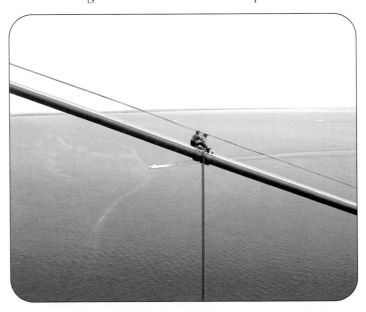

… but there's only one way to get there …

… and once you arrive you can feel pretty lonely.

on for fear of losing them, and a camera strap adds a whole new dimension to its security.

Most people just stare in awe from that perspective, seemingly on top of the world.

An unidentified veteran maintenance worker with many years on the job used to tell of the day when he was assigned to take some visitors to the top of the tower, which requires special arrangements. Not just anybody can go up there.

The visitors were accompanied through the route as described above and stood in awe of the Straits view like everyone else. A stiff wind was blowing.

One of the visitors engaged the maintenance worker in an extended conversation while the other visitor went to the other side of the tower walkway, the wind in his face.

Suddenly that visitor began fumbling with a small bag from within his jacket and held it over the rail to dump the contents over the side. Before the bridge worker could respond, the contents of the bag were blowing back onto the group on the walkway. Everyone's hair, faces and clothing were coated with a grayish powder.

It was then that the visitor explained that he came to scatter the ashes of a friend who had worked on the construction of the bridge, a noble

Cable lighting as it appeared when the bridge was being built.

Workmen wear safety harnesses to secure them while on dangerous areas of the bridge.

Street lights keep the highway illuminated on the bridge year-round.

idea but certainly not allowed. The visitor never considered the wind direction when carrying out his unusual duty.

The maintenance crew of the bridge has operated for years with a fierce personal pride, a sense of teamwork and a successful track record in their caretaking of the Big Mac. The job has been done all along with a familiarity that is similar to taking care of personal property. Inspections have repeatedly shown that the bridge's care far exceeds what is expected for maintenance of a civil project.

It's the only way to do the job, maintenance workers say.

Bridge worker Dick Campbell operated the Authority's boat, was a diver for underwater maintenance and inspections and also did painting and other projects.

Hard-hat divers relayed information to bridge foremen topside after inspecting foundations for piers and caissons. The work was cold, dangerous and tiring. The cumbersome dive suits of that era had a heavy brass helmet, lead shoes and were supplied with air from a surface compressor.

A plow truck clears the bridge of snow in the early years.

The toll plaza is a large area that must be kept cleared of snow for the safety of motorists using their brakes.

Maintenance workers don't salt the bridge in the winter, they apply a sand and gravel mix for traction. When it gets plowed into the lake, it's going right back to where it came from in the first place – the bottom of the lake.

The causeway is clear in this photo, but just ahead is a stretch that often drifts with wind-blown snow.

Spring clean-up involves scooping up sand and road dirt.

A bucket truck lifts a worker into position for cable maintenance.

In the year 2000 the causeway on the St. Ignace side was resurfaced.

Workmen clean up the road deck after a maintenance project in the early 1960s.

The bridge roadway must be re-paved like any other highway.

MAINTENANCE CREW MID-1980S: *Dick Sweeney, Dan Baier, Joe Viznaw, Ken Therrian, Jim Ecker, Pete LaChapelle, Ed Blair, Mickey Van Sickle, Dan Johnson, Bob Lindley, Al Stempki, Hilda Holmberg, Greg Shimkovitz, Fred Scott, Dick Campbell, Ray Marshall, Bob Blair, Bob Therrian, Ernest (Shady) Giacherio, Jack Winters, Orlando Doyle, Dave Pechta, Paul Davis, Roger Munson, Paul Tallman, Fred LaCross, Thom Price, Robin Smith, Lynn Closs, Randy Tatrow, Ed Lester, Bruce St. Antoine, Rick Fenner, Ron Bomia, Gary Jackson, Ed Nichols, Mark Stempky.*

2006 MAINTENANCE CREW: *Dan Johnson, Steve Campbell, Paul White, John Arnott, Glen Lewis, Rich Hillock, Brad Spring, Conrad Becker, Larry Antkoviak, Fred Spinella, Bob Cena, Bob Evans, James Gross, Charlie Harrington, Dan Merren, Mike Krull, Jeff Fogelsonger, John Tracy, Tom Moran, Cory Peterson, Paul Tallman, Bill Fitzpatrick, Dave Ulrich, Mark Kinjorski, Joe Shampine, Greg Goetz, Loren Blasing, Paul Matelski, Joe Visnaw, Todd Mayer, Todd Joseph.*

The Mackinac Bridge presents many geometric angles and shapes, including those in this view through the piers from the south side at Mackinaw City.

Pigeon and sea gull droppings have been eating away at the paint on the Mackinac Bridge for years and now double-crested cormorant poo can be added to the noxious mix, the Mackinac Bridge Authority's chief engineer said in 2006.

"We don't want them there," said Kim Nowack, who told the Petoskey News-Review she is looking for new ways to shoo the birds away. "The cormorants are the latest threat to the bridge. The bird droppings corrode the steel, and make maintenance harder by soaking up moisture and putting it against the steel."

She said the annual inspection report said the droppings were a detriment to the coating system but had not risen to the "major problem" category.

Nowack said the Authority had put screens on the box beams underneath where the pigeons like to nest, mainly toward the Mackinaw City end of the bridge. But the cormorants, which migrate to Michigan from Mississippi and Arkansas in the spring and return in late fall, are much larger and more voracious birds than pigeons and gulls.

9

Operations

The Operations Department of the Mackinac Bridge is really the pulse, the nerve center of the bridge. It is in the Administration Building's front offices that day-to-day decisions are made, hourly assessments figured, emergency measures taken and judgements decided to sometimes close the bridge for short periods of time.

The Operations Department moves vehicles, people and events across the span and coordinates this traffic – averaging 12,000 vehicles per day – around scheduled maintenance, weather and emergency conditions.

Although the main goal of the people who work in Operations is to keep the bridge open and running smoothly, dealing with closings is part of their job. It's a fact of life that has averaged out to occur about once a year in the 50-year history of the bridge.

The closings included shut-downs of two minutes each when presidents John F. Kennedy, Dwight D. Eisenhower and Harry S. Truman were buried.

Most of the time, however, weather is the chief factor when the bridge does close. Wind especially has played a role since the Authority adopted tighter safety restrictions in the aftermath of the Yugo going off the bridge in 1989.

As an example of the new protocol, the chart below lists a high number of closures in 1995-1996, a time period with a particularly rough winter:

In other years, the number of closures were minimal prior to 1989 and have also included falling ice and accidents as reasons for closure. Recent examples from the Operations Log include the date of April 18, 2003 when the bridge was closed for two hours and 55 minutes due to falling ice.

Notes from that day state:

"Ice falling from cables hitting all four lanes of traffic. 30-40 foot sheets of ice dropping to roadway. Temperature was holding at 32.1. The temperature and lack of wind accounted for the long closure. One day of freezing rain and falling temperatures caused the ice."

The conditions of ice falling from the bridge cables and towers usually occur when the temperature is just right to allow panes of ice to melt enough to fall away from the area where they are frozen. This

Date	Duration	Reason	Type
July 13, 1995	1 hour	Wind	Total
July 14, 1995	1 hour	Wind	Total
Dec. 6, 1995	2 hours	Wind/snow	Partial - High profile only
Dec. 9, 1995	3 hours	Wind/snow	Total
Jan. 29, 1996	5 hours	Wind/snow	Total
Jan. 30, 1996	6 hours	Wind/snow	Partial - High profile only
March 19, 1996	2 hours	Wind	Partial - High profile only
March 25, 1996	1 hour	Wind	Total

The Mackinac Bridge's Operations Department keeps traffic flowing on the span 24 hours a day, seven days a week, 365 days a year. The office ultimately decides when the bridge is restricted or closed for safety reasons.

can happen when the sun shines just right on the surface off the towers or the cables, causing the ice to let go. Bridge workers can spot problem areas with binoculars and almost predict which section will next fall. When the sun goes behind clouds or changes position enough to alter the effect, the condition passes.

The date of Aug. 27, 2003 brought a closure of 37 minutes due to a car fire on the bridge.

The log entry reads:

"Vehicle on fire southbound at mid-span. 08:43 Bridge closed to all traffic. St. Ignace Fire Department responding. Chief Engineer reports pavement damage, will need replacement in the fall. George's Wrecker removed burnt vehicle from bridge deck. Northbound traffic released at 09:13 and south-

bound traffic released at 09:20 after St. Ignace Fire Department cleared the bridge."

Most car accidents don't block the bridge for long, as emergency responders quickly clear the damaged vehicles and get traffic moving again. Injuries can make the process slower.

This is proven in the log entry for Oct. 27, 2002:

"Seven car chain reaction accident southbound at approximately Pier 3. Blocking all lanes to bring equipment in to remove vehicles from bridge. No serious injuries, a few minor. Closure for 53 minutes, 14:10 to 15:03."

Ironically, the highest wind speed ever recorded on the bridge didn't close it at all.

There wasn't time.

On May 9, 2003 a rapidly moving front at 4:08 p.m. produced a wind speed of 124 mph with marble-size hail, lasting one minute. It was all over just as quickly as it hit. There were no reported accidents or injuries. The anemometer readings topped the previous high of 117 mph, set on Sept. 10, 2001, when the highest wind gust on record was logged during another fast-moving front that passed through the Straits.

Bright sunshine on a winter day can sometimes melt ice that has accumulated on the bridge towers or suspension cables

The Mackinac Bridge Authority operated a bus system for several years to transport pedestrians across the span.

Severe weather can account for brief closures of the Mackinac Bridge, but it was completely closed less than 50 times in the first 50 years of its history.

Operations personnel watch a myriad of weather instruments, computer monitors and toll-collecting software from their windowed command center at the St. Ignace side of the bridge. It's the place where the action is, where situations are first recognized and dealt with. It takes a very particular type of person to balance all the activities, situations and stresses into an eight-hour shift in that job.

Besides weather radar and temperature gauges, wind speeds are recorded as far away as the White Shoal Lighthouse 15 miles to the west giving a heads-up to approaching weather conditions.

Monitors display and record all toll transactions from each lane, allowing supervisors to see the type of vehicle that is passing through and how much they are being charged. Toll collectors can easily report situations to a supervisor, who can then answer questions or relay concerns to the St. Ignace Post of the Michigan State Police, located across the street for easy access to the bridge and I-75 or US 2 to the north and west.

Tolls on the bridge have varied over the years,

increasing and decreasing with the political climate and financial responsibilities of the Mackinac Bridge Authority.

Using a two-axle passenger car as an example, a fare of $3.25 was charged when the bridge opened, a competitive rate to what the Michigan Department of Transportation ferries had received to take a vehicle and passengers across during the 1957 summer season.

The ferries moved nearly 870,000 vehicles in 1956, the last full year they were in operation, and the Mackinac Bridge had almost 1.5 million crossings the first full year it was open.

"A lot of those crossings that first year were out of curiosity," said Walter North, a top Authority administrator for 26 years. "People just wanted to drive over it. They didn't necessarily have a destination in the U.P. or in the Lower, it was something to see."

In 1960 a 25-cent increase was imposed, followed by another jump of a quarter in 1961.

"That's because the trust indenture between the Authority and the revenue bond buyers dictated that if you didn't make a certain percentage, 120 percent, of

Toll supervisor Lorraine Garries has worked for the Bridge Authority in several capacities over many years. There aren't too many situations that she hasn't dealt with coming through tollbooths during that time.

debt coverage to build up a cushion then you had to call in the consulting traffic engineers and they would recommend a schedule that would get that 120 percent."

On Jan. 1, 1969, the tolls dropped from $3.75 to $1.50, a huge reduction. The Michigan Legislature was ready to pass the Good Roads Package to improve the state's highways and wanted to increase the vehicle licensing fee and add a gasoline tax to pay for it.

Gov. George Romney attached a caveat to passage of the bill.

"Romney indicated that he would not sign the bill unless there was some relief in bridge tolls," said North. "He felt that the bridge overcame a physical barrier between the two peninsulas but that there was still a financial barrier with the toll being that high. They dropped the toll to $1.50 for passenger cars and put in that there would be a $3.5 million advance each year to offset the 60 percent drop in revenues. But it wasn't an outright grant, and that's why there's still a toll today."

Crossings increased by about 3 percent per year during the first 12 years of the bridge's operation, but a 21.9 percent increase came about in 1969 when the fare dropped to $1.50.

The rates stayed the same for the next 40 years, until an increase was enacted to help pay for needed repairs on the bridge. On May 1, 2003, the basic fare structure increased to $2.50 for passenger cars, $2 per

axle for motor homes, $3 per axle for trucks and buses and $1.50 per vehicle for commuters.

Immediate uses for the funding were to install a new security camera system that allows monitoring capabilities of the entire bridge, and a complete removal of the lead-based paint on the bridge and repainting with a zinc-oxide formula that will take more than 10 years and cost nearly $100 million. The paint job was made more costly due to the necessity for containment equipment and proper disposal of hazardous materials.

Commuters also had the option of paying by token or by a debit card issued by the Bridge Authority, as well as proximity cards and windshield transponders, introduced in 2004.

More than once in the bridge's first 50 years, politicians and local groups sought to end the toll collections altogether. A 1964 effort led to a petition drive and a 2005 campaign drew some statewide support. Both, however, failed

A dispute concerning who had control in making decisions about the Mackinac Bridge was legally put to rest in 2005.

Operations Manager Ben Wiggins stamps the state's check for deposit as bridge Authority Chairman Prentiss M. Brown hands a receipt over to Controller Donald Stearns. Larry Rubin looks on at left.

After dropping the bridge fare to $1.50, the state issued a check for $3.5 million as an advance to cover the 60 percent drop in revenues.

Gov. Jennifer M. Granholm signed legislation on Sept. 20 that officially codified the agreement between the Mackinac Bridge Authority and the Michigan Department of Transportation. The agreement and the four-bill package detailed the legal relationship between the Bridge Authority and MDOT for the first time since the reorganization of state government under the 1963 Constitution.

"The Mackinac Bridge is an enduring symbol of the beauty and grandeur of Michigan's two peninsulas," Granholm said. "The agreement signed earlier this year and the legislation I have signed today ensures that the Mackinac Bridge Authority will continue to serve as the guardian of this precious asset."

Under the agreement and the four-bill package, the Bridge Authority will continue to exercise its traditional independent decision-making role over matters involving the bridge, including risk management, insurance, engineering, inspection, and other services related to the operation, maintenance, repair, and improvement of the Mackinac Bridge.

The bills were introduced by state Sen. Jason Allen, R- Traverse City to confirm an agreement reached in September into state law. Similar legislation sponsored by Reps. Kevin Elsenheimer, R-Bellaire, and Tom Casperson, R-Escanaba was approved by the state House of Representatives.

The bills include mandates that:

Gov. Jennifer Granholm and Mackinac Bridge Authority Chairman William Gnodtke signed into law the agreement defining responsibilities and management roles of MDOT and the Authority on the Mackinac Bridge on Sept. 20, 2005.

- Repeal the section of law that stipulate that the Mackinac Bridge Authority will revert to Michigan Department of Transportation control once the bridge debt is paid, allowing the Authority to retain control of decision making in perpetuity.
- Specify that the Mackinac Bridge Authority is an autonomous entity within the Michigan Department of Transportation.
- Remove the stipulation that the state treasurer serve as treasurer of the Authority, allowing the Authority to manage the finances of the bridge.

- Outline the specific functions and responsibilities of the Mackinac Bridge Authority.

In addition, MDOT will continue to serve as the appointing authority for the executive secretary of the Authority after consultation with the Bridge Authority, and will work to implement decisions made by the Bridge Authority consistent with state law. MDOT will also provide the Bridge Authority with civil service personnel necessary for the Bridge Authority to perform its duties, assist with the purchasing of goods and services, and provide input and expertise on the state's transportation system. The legislation also safeguards Bridge Authority funds by

A 2005 law ensured that the Mackinac Bridge Authority will always maintain control of the structure's maintenance and finances.

Operations Manager Ben Wiggins instructs a bridge patrol officer before his next crossing. Patrolmen used to warn speeding motorists, but now leave that duty to the Michigan State Police.

requiring the state treasurer to maintain the funds in a dedicated amount.

"Just as the Mackinac Bridge represents an important connection between the Upper Peninsula and lower Michigan, this deal also reflects the strong partnerships that we can forge to better serve the citizens of our great state," said Representative Gary McDowell, D-Rudyard, whose district includes part of Cheboygan County. "This legislation represents a strong endorsement by the Legislature of the Governor's leadership in protecting the Mackinac Bridge."

McDowell, whose district also includes the Bridge and Bridge Authority headquarters, was a key advisor to the Granholm Administration in forging the agreement and developing a bi-partisan compromise on legislation to codify the agreement.

C. Edwin Haltenhoff, the Bridge Authority's first general manager.

Orlando Doyle, first maintenance manager of the Mackinac Bridge.

Personnel of the Mackinac Bridge Authority have their picture taken in front of the Administration Building.
Extreme back row, upper right, left to right: *C. E. Haltenhoff, General Manager; Lawrence A. Rubin, Executive Secretary. Group at left, "Operations", back row, left to right: Clyde O'Rourke, George Malnar, Wallace Burrell, Edward Lozon, Henry Devereaux, Frederick Paquin, Paul Faircloth, Marvin Mohr, Stanley Sunderland, Peter Everson, Isaac Carlberg, Louis Leville.* **Not shown are** *George Zack, Herman Winters and Archibald Cosens.* **Front row, left to right:** *Maurice Scanlon, Bernard Balbough, Richard Coffin, Glenn Gustafson, John Cortopassi, Raymond Kaminsky, Wallace Massaway, Clifford France, Benson A. Wiggins, Jr., Operations Manager.* **Middle group, top:** *Herman D. Ellis, Photographer—Public Information executive. Back row, left to right: Helen Powers, Donald Thompson, Joseph Gorman, Patricia Peach, Margaret Halava, Merle McLeod.* **Not shown is** *Harold Bell.*
Front row, left to right: Barbara Bentgen, Josephine Vecillo, Marie Roggenbuck, Donald Steams, Comptroller. **Right-hand group. Maintenance, back row, left to right:** *Orlando. Doyle, Maintenance Manager, Melvin LaChapelle, Richard Campbell, Donald Vigeant, Lerne Mclane, Stanley Cope, William Grogan, Donald Snyder, Lyle Grogan, Alfred Schlehuber.* **Front row, left to right:** *Elmor Gust, Charles Closs, Joseph Marchand, James Droski, Eugene Perry, Ernest Giacherio, and Robert Therrian.*

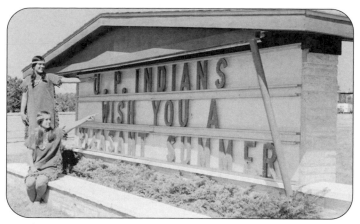

The Mackinac Bridge Authority's original marquee sign near the St. Ignace tollbooths…

… was replaced by a new, easily changed electrical model. A snowy owl was atop the sign the day this picture was taken.

The well-grounded Mackinac Bridge has survived several direct lightning strikes relatively unscathed. The bridge was designed to withstand 2 1/2 times all the recorded weather stresses of the Straits of Mackinac.

10

Escort Complete...

Webster's Dictionary defines "acrophobia" as "a morbid fear of being at a great height."

Since the bridge is 200 feet above the water at its highest point mid-span, it has become an obstacle for some people who cannot bear the thought of driving across.

In the first year of operation, the Mackinac Bridge Authority transported at least six jittery motorists across the five-mile span, including a hefty Detroit teamster truck driver.

In each instance, the drivers were afraid to make the crossing on their own and appealed to the Bridge Authority to have someone take the wheel for them.

In five cases that first year, the owners were content to surrender the wheel and make the trip while sitting alongside the driver. In another, however, the driver not only begged for help but begged not to be driven over in his own vehicle.

"He made the trip crouched in the back seat of a patrol car with his head below the windows," said Henry Devereaux, toll supervisor. "When we got to the other side, he offered me a $5 tip."

Bridge patrol officers say that more men than women ask for help, and that the shakes are worse at night than during the daytime.

"They just chicken out," Devereaux said.

The Motorist Assistance Program is free to "timid" drivers and provides a driver to get the vehicle to the other side. Cars, trucks, motorcycles and even semi-trail-ers have been driven across for frightened owners.

"They try to apologize," Chum Frazier said while he was operations manager in 1997, "but we say, 'You're not the only one.'"

By 1977, the number requesting help had risen to around 200 people annually and by 1987 reached 400. It continued to increase, and more than 1,300 motorists ask

Maintenance Manager Orlando Doyle displays the "flat car" designed for use by vehicles that got a flat tire on the Mackinac Bridge. A car's wheel could be driven onto the apparatus, locked into place and driven off the bridge.

for a driver each year these days, the Authority reports. Many are regulars, well-known to the escort personnel.

Timid southbound drivers can ask for an escort at the tollbooth, while northbound drivers can call from a courtesy phone. Patrol officers or maintenance workers drive vehicles across for those who can't handle it.

Those who grab the driver are the hardest to handle, Frazier says. He tries to keep them talking and tells them to look straight ahead at the roadway, not off to the sides.

"Some are so scared they feel like if they can grab hold of you, then you're their security," Frazier said. "We've had a lot start across and freeze up in the middle. We have to send someone out to pry their hands off the wheel."

One motorist-assist sent the escort driver to a van, where the female driver was visibly shaking with fear at the prospect of crossing the bridge. Nothing the driver said could calm the woman, who was unable to secure her seatbelt due to her shaky hands.

"Just about then I looked in the back of the van and it was full of cages with snakes inside – big ones," the escort driver recalled. "I asked if any of the snakes were poisonous, and she said they *all* were. And this lady was scared to drive across the bridge?"

Some drivers who cross the bridge are anything but afraid. They can be careless, bold and inattentive to their driving and distracted by the beautiful scenery.

In the bridge's early years, astonished tourists crossing for the first time would stop at various points on the bridge and get out of their cars to take pictures, unmindful that parking is forbidden on the bridge – part of Interstate 75.

In 1977, Larry Rubin reported that 82 cars ran out of gas while crossing the bridge. Bridge patrol vehicles carry gasoline onboard to help in these situations, and will donate enough fuel to get the vehicle running and complete the trip to either side, where gasoline is readily available.

By the year 2000, the number had grown to more than 360 cars per year – or an average of almost one per day – that would run out of gas on the bridge.

Another common call is to help a motorist who has experienced a mechanical breakdown on the bridge, of all places. While the Authority does not provide mechanical repairs as such on the bridge, their patrol cars are equipped with rubber spring-loaded bumpers to allow for pushing the disabled vehicles to one side or the other and mechanical help.

Bridge patrol officers used to warn motorists for speeding, but stopped the practice years ago when the Michigan State Police stepped up their presence on the bridge after they began operating from a brand new post adjacent to the tollbooths in St. Ignace.

The speed limit is 45 mph, and 20 mph for trucks and motorcoaches who use the right lane only and must

This phone booth and shelter house is for use by drivers and pedestrians seeking help crossing the Mackinac Bridge. It's located at Exit 337 at Mackinaw City on the northbound side.

Timid drivers are taken across the Mackinac Bridge by escort drivers. Paul Matelski heads back to a waiting patrol vehicle after driving a woman from St. Ignace to Mackinaw City in 2007.

keep their four-way flashers on and not pass anyone.

Once a Canadian woman was stopped for speeding on the bridge, traveling nearly 100 mph. When questioned, she had a simple explanation.

"I'm scared to death of this bridge," she told the patrolman, "so I want to get off it as soon as I can."

Motorists in a hurry sometimes get frustrated if they are stuck behind the escort of a large piece of equipment being trucked across the bridge or two halves of a modular home carefully being transported on the way to its destination.

But a truck driver once sued because he didn't get an escort and had an accident.

In 1994 an Indiana family was awarded more than $821,000 by a Court of Claims judge who ruled against the Mackinac Bridge Authority, stating that the Authority failed to take safety precautions that could have prevented the accident. Ingham County Judge William E. Collette wrote that warning signs should have been posted and escorts should have been provided for all traffic during a 1989 gale when independent

These speed limit lights, located at Pier 17, were later removed by the Bridge Authority.

Bridge worker Paul Matelski secures the ramps on the Mackinac Bridge Authority's snowmobile trailer after loading sleds for a trip north across the bridge. A snowmobile and driver crossed for as little as $1 in the early days of providing snow-sled transports. The costs later increased to $5 and was $10 in 2007. Sportsmen who enjoy long distance riding say it's still a bargain to be able to enjoy trails on both sides of the Straits.

truckers Eugene and Kathleen Horton were injured when their pick-up truck overturned and their aluminum trailer plummeted into the Straits.

Bridge workers that day escorted "high profile" vehicles traveling southbound, but made no accommodations for northbound trucks. The Authority maintained that the accident was caused by a force of nature, not negligence.

However, following the judge's decision the Authority changed its escort policy and now has weather warning signs on approaches leading to the bridge.

The Big Mac would be endangered daily by trucks transporting explosives, gasoline, acids and nuclear materials, were it not for the escort crews.

The average motorist isn't aware of what is just ahead of their vehicle and probably will never need to be concerned, thanks to the efficient system developed for safely escorting such cargoes across the Straits.

Mackinac Bridge Authority escort drivers do the job every day safely, silently and with the care that is needed to protect the bridge and its passengers.

Dangerous loads such as radioactive material, explosives, overwide and overweight vehicles must give two hours' notice of arrival. When these vehicles are escorted across the bridge the dangerous cargo moves in the outside lane, kept free of regular traffic between the escort and the truck. The caravan moves at 20 mph with flashers on and does not pass any other vehicle.

Trucks carrying gasoline and propane do not require special permits from the State Police Fire Marshall's Division in order to travel Michigan highways. Others, considered "placarded loads," have a metal sign that indicates the nature of their permit. Those trucks must wait for an escort before crossing the Mac.

Placarded loads cross the bridge daily, escorted by an Authority vehicle to ensure a safe transit.

Oversized loads of all shapes and sizes cross the bridge accompanied by an escort vehicle that controls the speed and lane use of the loaded truck.

After a training period, a trucker that must make multiple trips across the bridge can qualify for a bridge permit to cross without an escort if they follow the rules.

Although there have been accidents, mostly caused by ice and wind, thousands of placarded loads cross the bridge safely each year escorted by vigilant bridge escorts.

Another way that the bridge serves as a checkpoint of sorts is in the state of Michigan's efforts to control wood-borne insects that endanger forests.

In 2005, Michigan Gov. Jennifer Granholm declared May 22 through May 28 as "Emerald Ash Borer (EAB) Awareness Week," to increase public understanding and awareness of EAB.

A state officer reminded travelers to leave firewood at home during their travels throughout the year.

"Movement of firewood has caused artificial spread of EAB to parts of our state away from the generally infested quarantined area in southeast Michigan," said Department of Agriculture (MDA) Director Dan Wyant. "Camping and campfires are a great Michigan tradition, and should continue to be so, but it is extremely important to leave firewood at home and buy what you need when you get to your travel destination."

EAB is an invasive insect native to Asia, discovered in Michigan in 2002. EAB attacks ash trees in its larval stage, feeding undetected under the bark, which disrupts water and nutrient flow, eventually killing the tree. An estimated 15 million ash trees were already dead or dying in Michigan due to EAB infestations by 2006.

Twenty Michigan counties and 19 isolated infestations had been quarantined, making it illegal to move hardwood firewood or other regulated articles out of the quarantine into the balance of the Lower Peninsula. In addition, firewood and other regulated articles may not be moved out of the remainder of the Lower Peninsula of Michigan, designated by the quarantine as a "regulated area." This means no hardwood firewood can be moved into the Upper Peninsula or into surrounding states. Travelers are reminded that if they move regulated firewood, it could be confiscated, and fines could be issued to prevent the spread of EAB.

To further strengthen efforts to prevent firewood movement into the U.P., a livestock and plant checkpoint opened at the Mackinac Bridge. The checkpoint helped the state protect the U.P. from various livestock diseases and invasive exotic insects, including bovine tuberculosis and EAB.

Checkpoints were set up in Mackinaw City and St. Ignace to help enforce the laws.

An unusual escort took place with a little help from a cop who used some psychology – and maybe a little

Inspector David White of the Michigan Department of Agriculture's Pesticide and Plant Pest Management Division checks a load of pulp wood for a northbound trucker.

Firewood checkpoints are located in Mackinaw City and at St. Ignace.

help from above – during a 1987 attempt by a man to walk across the bridge carrying a large wooden cross.

"He was already on the bridge when we got the call," remembered Mike Madden, former Chief of Police in Mackinaw City. "He was walking across the country carrying the cross, which had wheels attached to the base so it would roll along. The Bridge Patrol called us because he refused to allow their pick-up truck to carry him across. He said it was God's will that he had to walk every inch of the way – no rides."

Madden pleaded with the man in a special way.

"I wound up asking him if he wouldn't kneel with me, right there on the bridge deck," Madden recalled. "After he was quiet in prayer for a few minutes, with all these people standing around him, I whispered and asked if he'd heard Him."

The man opened his eyes and asked what Madden meant.

"I shook my head and said, 'You mean you didn't hear Him? It's OK. He said it's OK for this one stretch to ride in the truck. Just this one time.'"

According to Madden the man beamed a big smile, got up off his knees and allowed bridge workers to place the cross in the back of the truck and hopped in the front seat.

"I heard a few snickers from the other policemen and bridge workers and said, 'I guess not all of you heard Him either,' and the man was on his way with his cross."

Wind conditions of 30 mph prompt escorts for high-profile vehicles, including trucks, buses, campers and trailers hauling boats. Vehicles with loose items in a truck bed or on a trailer are slowly escorted across for safety's sake. November storms are notorious for this.

Mysteries of Pier 17

While building the Mackinac Bridge, workmen and engineers began to notice that conditions in the Straits often seemed different in the area of Pier 17, the bridge's south anchor block. Winds were more intense, vibrations more noticeable and once the bridge opened vehicles sometimes experienced an uplift or sway as they crossed the pier.

In fact, most wind incidents on the bridge seem to occur at Pier 17. It has also been the scene of many staged events and posed photographs, although it is illegal for motorists to stop there or park. In the early days people stopped there all the time to take in the panoramic view, one of two locations – Pier 22, the north anchor block, is the other – with a spot on the east and west sides of the bridge traffic lanes to tempt them.

As the first construction project while the bridge was being built, Pier 17's reputation began early. The first crane operator assigned to the job of helping to build the rising center walls of the anchor block's superstructure quit as soon as he saw the trestle-perch on which he had to work.

After the bridge was open for business, early windstorms prompted a "buddy system" to be established whereby drivers of trucks and other heavily-loaded, solid vehicles were requested to escort lighter-weight vehicles by driving across on their windward side. The system worked well, unless the driver of a car got impatient and took off before the

crossing was complete – or they hit a sudden gust of wind, usually at Pier 17.

A day famous on the Great Lakes for incredible winds – Nov. 10, 1975, when the ore carrier Edmund Fitzgerald sank in Lake Superior – was also the day a southbound tractor-trailer combination toppled over onto the compact car it was escorting. The accident happened at Pier 17.

"I remember going out there with a crane crew to

Pier 17's mysterious beginnings included a crane operator who quit his first day on the job upon seeing the small platform where he would work, high above the water.

try and turn the truck right-side up," recalled Nelson LaPointe of Mackinaw City. "The winds were so strong we couldn't walk on the roadway to try and set the crane up. We had to wait until it calmed down."

Miraculously, no one was seriously injured. The compact car had been flattened, and bridge workers safely retrieved the owner's dog. Later it was determined that the tractor-trailer was empty, which made the vehicle no match for winds of that stature, measured at up to 90 mph.

The truck driver was slightly injured and refused transport to the nearest hospital five miles back in St. Ignace because he would not return across the bridge. Instead, he was taken to Cheboygan for treatment, 20 miles from the accident scene.

On another occasion, a group of snowmobilers, happy after a trip to the Upper Peninsula, returned to the Straits Area pulling a small trailer with their sleds and other gear. They paid the fare for car and trailer at the tollbooth, then traveled across the bridge to their homes in Mackinaw City.

Upon arrival at the first house, the men found the trailer missing.

"The call came in that they thought their trailer must have blown off the bridge," Mackinaw City Patrolman Bob Desy remembered. "I called the bridge and their officers took a trip across and didn't find it on the roadway. The guys insisted it had to be there or else in the water, and the Mackinac County Sheriff went out there too but couldn't find it either. By then it was dark, and I decided to take a trip across to see for myself if any of their items could be found."

Desy said he figured the trailer was long gone until he spotted something piled into a corner of Pier 17 – the trailer, with the snowmobiles intact with all their gear.

This view from Pier 17 portrays a placid scene on the Straits that can dramatically change in about 20 minutes when a storm passes through.

The crane later toppled over under high winds on Pier 17 as the bridge was being built.

"It was overturned in a way that made it next to invisible," Desy said. "It was hidden on that anchor block and driving by I could see how the others missed it. The men said they never felt it leave their car."

On Oct. 17, 1984, a precursor of what was to occur five years later almost happened when two Michigan Technological University students narrowly escaped death while driving across the bridge at 12:26 a.m.

Dawn M. Shawen, 18, and Krista K. Ball, 18, were northbound on the Mackinaw City side of the bridge span. Just after passing Pier 17, the car, driven by Shawen, hit the median, causing it to come back across two lanes and hit the curb along the edge of the bridge.

After hitting the curb, the car jumped up onto the rail where it rode for about 110 feet, precariously balanced above the Straits of Mackinac. The car's rear axle broke, and it fell back onto the bridge, noted Bill Reed of the Mackinaw City Police Department. No injuries were reported.

A 1998 accident, like many others, saw the same

Pier 17 is the only bridge support that has undergone serious structural repair work in a preventive-maintenance effort. Tons of stone were placed around the foundation to bolster support of the anchor block. Various steel bonds have been added underwater to ensure the integrity of the concrete mass.

guard rail react as it was designed to perform under a lower-speed collision.

Susan Anderson of Cheboygan lost control of her car on Jan. 21 at 7:50 a.m. and slid into the lower guardrail, tearing the front fender off her car.

"The bridge did what it is supposed to do," said Administrator Hank Lotoszinski. "It contained the vehicle. The front wheels locked in on the curbing, and it peeled off the front bumper."

Past the safety rail is a three-pipe guard railing. Anderson's car did not touch the second railing, Lotoszinski said. No one was injured.

Currents that flow past the pier are visibly strong from the bridge deck, and look ominous when viewed from an airplane or atop the south tower. In 2006, ultra-marathon swimmer Jim Dreyer reported being pushed far off course as he passed Pier 17 in his quest to set a swimming endurance record at the Straits.

But not all of the bridge's Pier 17 tales have unfortunate endings.

In 1995, Julie Engel got worried when her boyfriend's truck seemed to be faltering in the middle of the span. Andrew Nelson pulled off onto Pier 17, where it's illegal to stop or park. A State Trooper saw

A speaker provides communication from the Authority's offices to Pier 17. The locked tube accesses a ladder to the base of the anchor block.

the vehicle turn off and approached, but must have feared the worst when he saw the young couple exit the vehicle and walk towards the front of the car and the edge of the anchor block.

With the Straits 150 feet below, the Trooper was about to call for back-up to assist him with the situation when Nelson's motive became clear. In the glare of the headlights, he dropped to one knee, produced a tiny box with a ring inside, and proposed to Engel.

She accepted.

Today Pier 17 is monitored by a video camera like all other locations on the bridge. In addition, a speaker system allows Authority officials to talk to someone on the anchor block – undoubtedly to warn them to move along.

Pier 17 provides a tempting – but illegal – parking spot on the bridge. Patrol cars sometimes park there to watch for speeders. This is also the place where the bridge's first birth occurred in 1983.

Pier 17's interior was hollow while being built, eventually housing the cablestays that anchor the bridge's support system.

The hollow interior of Pier 17 reveals the place where the suspension cables are anchored.

Utra-marathon athlete Jim Dreyer fought strong currents in the Straits during his 2006 attempt to set a new swimming endurance record.

New signage warns motorists not to stop on the bridge for picture taking, sightseeing or any other non-emergency purpose.

The circumstances that involved a birth on the bridge at Pier 17, the bridge's south anchor block, would be an exception but most all other stops made by drivers there would be subject to prosecution, a bridge official said.

"This is due to federal legislation brought by the Department of Homeland Security," noted Dean Steiner, operations manager of the Mackinac Bridge. "There are locations that are now protected for security reasons and the bridge is one of them."

In the past, the four locations — two to each anchor pier — seemed an ideal spot to take a picture or view the scenic Straits of Mackinac by unknowing tourists. Others have climbed the high curbs to negotiate a U-turn on the bridge.

Officials seem to have determined that the "No Parking" signs painted onto the concrete interior walls of the piers aren't enough. Under the new law, a quick unauthorized visit to the pier could mean a visit of far longer duration in jail.

Crossing Under

Over the course of the first 50 years, it would be impossible to tally the number of ships, boats, watercraft and yachts that have crossed under the Mighty Mac. The number would be in the tens of thousands – more than a hundred thousand, perhaps many more, but how many?

There have been naval vessels, U.S. Coast Guard cutters, U.S. submarines and ships built and launched in Great Lakes shipyards and bound for new homeports.

Giant freighters, tankers, passenger vessels, tugboats and fleet barges have passed under the span. So have tall ships, wooden schooners and brigantine replicas of a bygone era, sails billowing from masts and complex rigging.

Flotillas of race boats use the Mackinac Bridge as a visual "finish line" when completing the Chicago to Mackinac yacht race each July, with the real end coming at Windermere Point on Mackinac Island.

Ferryboats have carried passengers under the bridge to glimpse the giant suspension bridge or to take tourists for a cruise just to marvel at the spectacle.

When it comes to commercial shipping seen on the Straits, there are two distinct categories of vessels that route courses under the Mackinac Bridge.

There are "lakers" and there are "salties."

A "laker" is a ship that stays within the Great Lakes, usually carrying iron ore, taconite pellets, finished steel or limestone to ports on Lake Michigan, Lake Huron or Lake Superior. They might travel empty for one leg of their journey, but begin passages early in the spring as soon as the Soo Locks open and usually work through the "gales of November" until winter lay-up time, depending on schedules and the ultimate closing of the locks.

A "salty" is a ship that comes through the St. Lawrence Seaway to bring cargo to Midwest ports, often staying to transit cargos within the lakes for the

A "salty" running empty, bound for a Great Lakes port to pick up new cargo. A ship like this ends up back in the ocean at the end of the summer season.

A "laker," like this giant ore carrier, continues its work within the Great Lakes.

The Mackinac Bridge averages 12,000 vehicles crossing in each 24-hour period, and can handle a maximum capacity of 6,000 vehicles per hour.

summer to "earn their keep" before eventually leaving in the fall with a load of grain or wheat, bound for an ocean voyage to a foreign destination.

But ships are not all that have passed under the Mac.

In a stunt that most pilots might have merely dreamed of, Capt. John Lappo performed a feat not to be forgotten and probably never again repeated on April 24, 1959 when he flew a giant U.S. Air Force bomber under the suspension span of the Mackinac Bridge at high speed.

Capt. John Lappo

Lappo, a 39 year-old Reconnaissance Aircraft Commander at the time, was in command of a six-engine B-47E Stratojet on a clear, mild Friday morning returning to Lockbourne Air Force Base near Columbus, Ohio from England. Wanting to show his crew the new Mackinac Bridge, he dipped the jet low towards the Straits of Mackinac and told his crew, "Hang on – we're going under that bridge."

The crewmen, used to Lappo's daring nature, likely knew he could pull it off. One member, a young navigator, wasn't so sure.

At an altitude of 75 feet, Lappo had less than 100 feet of clearance beneath the underside of the bridge superstructure as he aimed his plane between the 552-foot towers. According to reports, only two vehicles were on the suspended portion of the bridge when the B-47 roared through the Straits and under the Big Mac. A member of a work crew on the bridge later recalled the incident with disbelief.

"He was very lucky, I'll tell you that," said Dick Campbell of Lappo. "We had double-ended spiders –

like scaffolds – hanging from under the bridge. There were cables that were strung from each end, and we used to let them hang all the way to the water just in case somebody wound up falling. That way, they might have a chance to grab a cable and keep from drowning.

"Well, if that jet had hit one of those steel cables at the speed he was traveling, it might have sliced one of his wings," Campbell added. "An explosion could have been disastrous for the workmen, the crew of the jet, and the passengers on the bridge structure. It was a very large airplane, but it all happened very fast. We probably heard more of the roar of his engines after he passed under the bridge, we really didn't hear him coming until he was almost on us."

Lappo went down in history for his daredevil feat, and reported in an interview many years later that "it was a thrill."

The navigator that day mentioned the stunt to his father, an Air Force general. The Air Force was neither amused nor impressed and Lappo paid dearly for his

Many military pilots have flown over the Mackinac Bridge, but resisted the temptation to fly under it.

brash flying, losing his pilot's wings. Lappo pleaded guilty in a military court to flying closer than the 500-foot limit over water when not landing and lost his privilege to fly. He had, after all, risked the lives of his crew and a $3.5 million plane, the military said.

Despite losing his wings, Lappo remained a patriot and professed a great love for the Air Force. He was later promoted to the rank of major and then served in Vietnam on the ground as an aircraft maintenance officer. He retired as a lieutenant colonel.

Campbell logged 24 years as a maintenance worker and diver on the Mackinac Bridge and said that Lappo's plane wasn't the only one to attempt the stunt over the years.

"Oh, there've been several that have done it, military and private planes," Campbell recalled. "Back then we never thought too much about it working on the bridge. We just figured they'd get caught, especially the military planes."

Today a pilot would face Federal Aviation Administration sanctions if caught – and certainly would be reported – according to Mackinac Bridge Authority Administrator Robert Sweeney.

"There are laws today regarding the clearance of the shipping channel as well as the clearance of the bridge itself," Sweeney explained. "We've even had a couple of helicopters get too close to the bridge and they've been reported. Something like that scares motorists as well as our maintenance crews and we don't want them distracted wondering what's going on."

Sweeney stated that while concerns of this nature have heightened since Sept. 11, 2001, the laws themselves have been around much longer. He referred to a copy of the FAA laws pertaining to "minimum safe altitudes" which state that no person may operate an aircraft below "an altitude of 1,000 feet above the highest obstacle within a horizontal radius of 2,000 feet of the aircraft," or "closer than 500 feet to any person, vessel, vehicle or structure."

"These laws have been on the books for quite awhile," he said. "The FAA is in charge of the consequences a pilot would face for something like that."

The Mackinac Bridge also has patrol officers on duty who could report such an occurrence, as well as video cameras that would capture an image revealing an airplane's registration numbers as proof.

John Lappo died of pneumonia in 2003, at the age of 83, following a long battle with Parkinson's disease.

In an interview four years before his death, he did not say the stunt was worth his punishment, but with a twinkle in his eye he did admit to one regret.

"I wish I had had the chance to fly under the Golden Gate Bridge in San Francisco," Lappo declared.

The U.S. Air Force's B-47E Stratojet.

There is only one area where automobile traffic can pass *under* the Mackinac Bridge. Although West Central Avenue in Mackinaw City passes under a viaduct that is part of the highway approaching the bridge, there are indeed two roadways that pass under the bridge itself on the south shore of the Straits.

The first, and closest to the water, is a driveway in the parking lot at the entrance to Colonial

Michilimackinac in Mackinaw City. With plenty of clearance, the two-way drive allows motorcoach traffic that often brings groups to the fort as well as automobiles.

Nearby is North Huron Street, which becomes Straits Avenue after it crosses under the bridge. With only 10 feet, 6 inches of clearance it could well be the only flaw in the design of the Mackinac Bridge.

Although storm drains were installed and the original plans were for the street beneath the bridge

The overpass at Colonial Michilimackinac's entrance allows plenty of room for all traffic…

… but North Huron Street changes over to Straits Avenue under this 10-foot 6-inch clearance bridge.

Despite signs, flashing lights, and posted warnings…

…several trucks, motor homes and buses try it each year with unfortunate results.

to drop considerably below the height of the surrounding roadway, it was not completed that way.

For years, police have answered calls about oversized vehicles getting stuck under the span or ramming the bridge, close to the park entrance of Colonial Michilimackinac.

Trucks, buses, RV's, motorhomes and anything else taller than 10 feet, 6 inches have managed to get into trouble when the drivers of those vehicles ignored signage and drove under the low bridge.

Flashing lights and signs have made no difference for distracted drivers that paid no attention and felt a sickening crunch above on their roof. Air conditioning units atop larger vehicles have become an especially familiar sight to arriving officers, who find them on the

side of the road after being clipped by the bridge and dismembered from buses and recreational vehicles.

Many a driver has learned a difficult lesson by wondering what happened while crossing under the overpass. When they get out and walk back to the entrance, they see the signs and warning lights that they somehow missed.

Sailors in the Chicago-to-Mackinac Yacht Race have looked to the bridge as the last stretch before the finish line dating back to the mid-1950s when the bridge was being built.

A storage barn was squeezed under the Mackinac Bridge in 2005 on its way back to the grounds of the Old Mackinac Point Lighthouse in Mackinaw City. The barn, built in 1892 — the same year as the lighthouse — was moved to nearby property owned by the Mackinac State Historic Parks in 1961. When clearance was well under an inch below the bridge, workmen from the J & R Building Movers, Inc., of Petoskey studied the problem and let some air out of the trailer rig's tires. A chimney mount was eventually removed to allow passage of the barn to its original home.

After clearing a track through Straits ice for 62 years...

...the original U.S. Coast Guard Cutter Mackinaw crosses under the bridge for the last time before retiring to Mackinaw City for use as a museum ship.

The Pride of Baltimore is one of the many tall ships to pass under the Mighty Mac.

In 1959, the Royal Yacht Brittania sailed under the bridge with Her Royal Majesty Queen Elizabeth II. The ship was accompanied by a destroyer escort that followed to provide security.

"The Queen came out on deck and saluted the bridge as they crossed under," said Larry Rubin, bridge administrator at the time. "We stopped traffic as the Brittania approached and crossed under. People on the bridge honked their horns for her. It was quite the thing."

The tall ship Pride of Baltimore, reminiscent of a bygone era, sails through the fog under the Mackinac Bridge.

The Mackinac Bridge at mid-span, a glorious sight from water level.

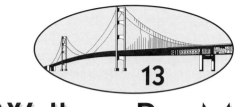

13

Walking Big Mac

There are many legal ways to cross the Mackinac Bridge in various motor vehicles, in parades, organized bicycle events or running races. But to the average person who would simply enjoy walking across the Big Mac, there's only one way to do it and only one date when it can be done.

Over the years, hundreds of thousands of people have walked across the bridge on Labor Day but the event had a humble beginning.

An early race-walk winner receives congratulations from Bob Davis (center), who went on to become a U.S. Congressman for the state of Michigan.

In 1958, the International Walkers Association proposed a walking race across the bridge to be held during the June dedication festivities. Previously, the Mackinac Bridge Authority had denied many requests from people who wanted to cross the bridge in an unusual fashion. Some wanted to cross by unicycle, to be pushed across in a wheelbarrow or to drive their car across backwards. A few wanted to walk.

The Authority granted the request for an organized walking effort and on June 25 history was made when 60 people showed up from the International Walkers Association to walk across. Despite the fog and rain, Michigan Gov. G. Mennen Williams fired a starting pistol on the bridge's south side at Mackinaw City and 55 minutes later the winner crossed the finish line at St. Ignace. Williams himself arrived just 10 minutes later.

Larry Rubin championed the idea of making the bridge walk an annual event and in 1959 the second bridge walk was held, this time on Labor Day. About 250 racers and pleasure walkers combined to cross, with the date changed from late June to the end

Larry Rubin

of summer to try and promote vacation travel to lengthen the tourist season through the end of August. At this point formal racing classifications were added for men, boys, women and girls. The races were sanctioned by the Michigan Amateur Athletic Union in 1960 and the turnout doubled to 500 people.

During one of those early races, young Greg Teysen of Mackinaw City decided to participate despite having no experience in race-walking and not owning a pair of running shoes like athletes today would wear.

"My mother suggested that I would need shoes with good support," Teysen recalled years later. "I had a pair of tennis shoes, but the best ones that fit that description were my black leather dress shoes. My dad thought I should wear two pairs of socks in case I got blisters. I had no idea the kind of trouble I was in."

Teysen began the race and eventually spread out from his competitors. Soon he began to feel pain in his feet, but steadfastly continued across the five-mile bridge.

"I was really hurting, but I could see the finish line coming up ahead," he continued. "Just then a kid about my age came up along side me and I asked him if he was in the same age division as I was. He said that he was, so we hoofed it pretty good the rest of the way and I beat him by one second and won my division. If he had said any other age group I would have let him pass me by, but his honesty cost him, I guess.

"When I crossed the line, I sat down right away to rest without cooling down," Teysen added. "Several minutes later my feet were in real distress and when I tried to get up my legs were so cramped I could barely walk. I finished third the next year with different shoes but I'll never forget that first crossing in those black leather shoes."

Soon, casually walking the bridge with family and friends became more popular than race-walking across.

The numbers increased to 1,500 in 1961 and 2,500 in 1962. As more participants arrived the logistics of the event became an issue, with transportation of the walkers becoming impossible with just the two buses

Bridge Walk Poster - circa 1960.

owned by the Authority. They needed a ride from one side of the bridge to the other – before or after the walk – and toilet facilities were not available to serve that many people, especially on the St. Ignace side.

To try and fix the problem of hosting a bigger and bigger party each year, the St. Ignace Chamber of Commerce stepped up and planned to transport 4,000 walkers to downtown St. Ignace after the 1963 event so that people could shop or get something to eat instead of all trying to get a ride southbound at once.

More growing pains ensued when too many of the participants were forced to wait in the rain for hours waiting for one of the 17 buses pressed into service to arrive.

In 1964, the direction was alternated to begin in St. Ignace and finish in Mackinaw City and it has been that way ever since. When 6,000 people showed up

that year, organizers realized that the event had become something that consisted mostly of walkers from the Lower Peninsula who wanted to return home promptly after they finished. Today walkers come from all across America.

The Mackinaw City Chamber of Commerce tried a different approach, issuing numbered certificates to bridge walkers that corresponded with numbers posted in the windows of merchants, redeemable for $1,500 worth of prizes. The program succeeded on several fronts – people thought the idea was fun and the stores enjoyed a busy day of business, plus the Mackinac Bridge Authority could now get a fairly accurate count of the number of people who had walked across. Today St. Ignace and Mackinaw City continue the gimmick.

Early bridge walks had small crowds, but the enthusiasm for the activity grew over the years to what it is today – the largest participation event in Michigan.

In the coming years the word got out that walking the Mackinac Bridge on Labor Day was a fun thing to do for families, groups, lovers, retirees – it seemed that every walk of life was represented. The Mackinac Bridge Walk had become so popular that an average of 15,000 people walked in 1966, 1967 and 1968.

History was made in 1966 when Michigan Gov. George Romney crossed in 57 minutes, beating the 65-minute crossing of Williams in 1958. In 1967 Romney cut 10 minutes off his time, doing it in 47 minutes. It should be pointed out that these men crossed with long-legged strides, an athletic feat short of running across but still a five-mile workout by anyone's defi-

Michigan Gov. George Romney hustled across the bridge in 57 minutes in 1966, forcing Larry Rubin (at right) and others to hoof it at the same brisk speed.

nition. The normal crossing time for casual walkers is about two hours.

The next Michigan electoral winner, Gov. William G. Milliken, accompanied a crowd of 16,000 who walked the bridge – and many wanted to share the experience with the new governor. The picture-taking and hand-shaking slowed him down to a 51-minute crossing. It wasn't until 1970 that Milliken clocked an elapsed time of 46 minutes and 50 seconds, a record that stood for many years as the fastest gubernatorial crossing and is still the fastest that any governor has *walked* across the bridge. Milliken did so among a crowd of more than 20,000 walkers that year.

Different Michigan governors have put their own stamp on the way they crossed the bridge. Gov. James Blanchard, a smiling personality who attracted crowds everywhere he went, was in no hurry and walked while carrying on conversations with those around him. Thousands would drive home and tell their friends that they had walked the bridge with Jim Blanchard, and they would be correct.

Gov. John Engler casually pushed a stroller across with his triplet daughters aboard. He was accompanied by the most visible security force for any governor on a Mackinac Bridge Walk in 50 years.

Gov. Jennifer Granholm, a runner who encouraged fitness among Michigan citizens, took off and ran across the bridge in 2003, her first year in office, and beat all previous crossing times by past governors. She encouraged the Mackinac Bridge Authority to develop a "fun-run" race prior to the walking event, and always ran with her family or other children invited to join in. For safety reasons, runners were selected by lottery from each of Michigan's 83 counties and several state agencies to enjoy the honor, restricting the numbers who could run with Granholm to around 300. There was never a shortage of applicants from anywhere in the state.

Michigan Gov. Jennifer Granholm has run across the Big Mac with groups of children…

…and with her family to promote physical fitness in the state. In 2005 she broke the ribbon at the finish line with her husband Daniel Mulhern.

People who are unable to walk across the bridge have found a place in the governor's running event…

…which precedes the annual Bridge Walk early on Labor Day morning.

Over the years, many participants returned from all over America and from countries around the world. They made the Mackinac Bridge Walk an annual event, proudly displaying patches that commemorated their feat. As the crowds grew, so did the number of unusual occurrences that had everyone talking on the way home. Some promoters, lobbyists and protesters figured that it was pretty hard to pass up the chance to work a crowd of that size.

Groups of all types and descriptions have walked the Mac over the years. Bands have played as they marched across and veterans' groups have carried the flag in color guards that walked the five miles. A ballerina once danced her way across on her tip-toes and another year a square-dance group managed to do-si-do their way across. Political statements have been

The growth of the Mackinac Bridge Walk can be seen in these photos taken at 10 a.m. in 1974...

... and at 10 a.m. in 2004. An average of 50,000 to 60,000 people have participated in recent years.

made and opinions have been expressed about war, peace and other worldly subjects the same as those who wore local campaign slogans on T-shirts or caps with union logos.

They all come to the Straits of Mackinac on Labor Day.

One year a young man from Wisconsin wore an Uncle Sam suit and walked across on stilts that were eight feet high. Another year two marriages were performed on Pier 22, the north anchor block that holds the cables. A reporter described the nuptials as "a wedding attended by 25,000 guests."

In 1979, Jack LaPorte of Flint decided to swim the Straits of Mackinac on Labor Day while throngs of others walked across. He did so in three hours. LaPorte was not the first to swim the Straits, but may have been the first to do so during the Bridge Walk.

One year the American Agricultural Movement members drove their heavy farm machinery out onto the bridge and dumped foreign meat over the side to protest the import of foreign meat products.

Naturally, anything that created a safety hazard, broke traffic laws or inconvenienced the walkers was

Mackinac Bridge workers begin setting up for the event a week before Labor Day.

One year a square-dance club danced their way across the Big Mac.

By two days before the Bridge Walk, workmen have installed lane dividers for safety purposes.

handled by security forces on the bridge. The Labor Day festival is made possible by the cooperative effort of local law enforcement agencies and the Michigan State Police. The Michigan National Guard continues security on the actual bridge span. Lost children are re-united with their parents, directions are given to walkers to help find parked automobiles and first-aid and water is administered to those in need. The U.S. Coast Guard patrols the waters below along with sheriff's department boats. A massive army of local volunteers in Mackinaw City and St. Ignace are also on the job from 4 a.m. until well past noon to make it all happen.

By 1983 the numbers were up to 43,000 walkers and 70 area school buses from throughout Northern Michigan. The plan had by then perfected, with walkers from either side riding a bus across from Mackinaw City to St. Ignace and walking from St. Ignace to Mackinaw City. The order in which they did so depended on their starting and finishing points. Rules had been established for the crossing that prevented animals except seeing-eye dogs, wagons and

other items.

The crowds increased steadily until 1992, when an unprecedented visitor arrived to walk the Mackinac Bridge – the President of the United States. President George H. W. Bush led an array of local political leaders, gawkers and Secret Service agents across that day. His long strides kept him well ahead of the estimated crowd of 85,000 which also crossed, an all-time record. More than 125 buses and transport

Bridge Walk participants are up early to catch the bus in Mackinaw City.

By mid morning, 120 buses are still making round-trips to keep the crowds flowing.

vehicles were summoned to move the crowds from point to point.

The First Lady, Barbara Bush, walked for a short time and rode the rest of the way in the presidential limousine. The president himself hopped into the limo just short of the finish line, disappointing the crowd that had gathered to greet him in Mackinaw City.

Bush's appearance marked the only occasion to date when Secret Service agents and sharpshooters were visible in the Straits area. No memories seem to

exist of security forces when John F. Kennedy campaigned at the bridge in 1960, but his stay was brief.

Bush arrived on Air Force One at Chippewa County Regional Airport at Kinross, Mich., and spent the night before the event at the Ramada Ojibwa Hotel in Sault Ste. Marie.

With 1992 being a presidential election year, many people showed up with signs for the other candidates, Bill Clinton and Ross Perot. Walkers had to pass through metal detectors in a fenced area, where a dumpster stood by. Officials, not from the Mackinac

President George H.W. Bush walked the bridge in 1992, flanked by local Republican supporters. Michigan's First Lady, Michelle Engler, was to the left of the President. Secret Service agents were at the four corners of the group, and other undercover police lined the rear of the throng. Many reported that they had difficulty matching Bush's long-legged pace.

Bridge Authority, told the non-Republican groups of people "no signs on the bridge" – a rule still enforced today – and collected the campaign materials as garbage. However, signs for Bush *were* allowed onto the bridge, creating a controversy about the fairness of the proceedings.

Bush did not carry Michigan in 1992, and did not win the election. Clinton did.

Subsequent attendance numbers dropped to the normal established range of 50,000 – 60,000 after the president's visit, where they have remained ever since; 62,500 walked in 1999, 65,000 in 2000 and the event is still the world's greatest walking event and has become a unique Michigan tradition.

In 1994, 14 people from an organ-transplant group showed up to prove their good health. Among their membership were those who had had a heart transplant, a liver transplant, and a woman who said she was the recipient of the first-ever double lung transplant. They all made it across.

Some laid claim to the fact that they had walked the bridge every year the event had been held, like Don Grieger of Mackinaw City. In 2004, he had walked it 44 straight years and and had the commemorative patches to prove it.

Others would sometimes walk the span, hop on the bus and ride back over to St. Ignace and do it again. Ray LaCombe of Mackinaw City used to outdo everyone – he always walked across more than once but some years he was able to complete four crossings

Styles of clothing and automobiles change but walking the Mackinac Bridge on Labor Day has been a consistent Michigan tradition since 1958.

in a single day.

The event has also been conducive to romance. In 1989 Randy and Cindy Klein of West Bloomfield, Mich., say they met while separately buying bus tickets in Mackinaw City for their crossing to St. Ignace. In 1992 they returned together and after crossing the finish line in Mackinaw City he proposed.

She accepted.

In 1993 they came back to get married at Colonial Michilimackinac, the historic fort that is entered from a building under the bridge at Mackinaw City. A year later they were back as a married couple and walked it again to celebrate their anniversary.

Weather can make the day a glorious adventure, or turn it into a cold soggy ordeal; but remarkably there have been few Labor Days that have been so miserable that the walk has been curtailed in any way. Weather in the Straits at that time of year has proven to usually be delightful. None of the bridge walks have ever been completely canceled, rain or shine, in the first 50 years, although the 1998 event was cut short by severe thunderstorms.

With the huge crowds that gather each year, some people get separated from family members; others get

Bridge walkers have come from all across Michigan, all across America…

… and all across the world to say they walked across the Mackinac Bridge.

lost or can't remember where they parked their cars.

A greeting platform is set up on the Mackinaw City side to welcome finishers in the event and introduce dignitaries. The site serves as a meeting place for those who walk at varying speeds or realize they may get separated.

The late Stan McRae of Mackinaw City served as master of ceremonies at this location for 30 years. Others have continued the tradition since, providing information and serving as a communications link for bridge walkers.

Labor Day morning is an early start for bridge walkers who begin lining up as early as 5 a.m.

The traditional route to walk the Mackinac Bridge begins in St. Ignace and ends in Mackinaw City. A fleet of 120 school buses work to carry crowds in the other direction, as needed.

49th Annual
MACKINAC BRIDGE WALK

THIS IS TO CERTIFY THAT

_____

Walked Across the World's Greatest Bridge,
September 4, 2006 from St. Ignace to Mackinaw City, Michigan.

SPONSORS:
Mackinac Bridge Authority
St. Ignace Chamber of Commerce
Mackinaw Area Chamber of Commerce

Jennifer M. Granholm, Governor

31001

A certificate is awarded to each finisher of the Mackinac Bridge Walk.

14

Bridge Parades

When high winds dictate that traffic must be escorted across the Mackinac Bridge at slow speeds, there's a very good purpose for doing so.

When other traffic makes an escorted crossing of its own choosing, it's for another reason entirely – to have a parade.

Over the years, many different types of groups have arranged with the Mackinac Bridge Authority to cross as a group. It's fun and exciting, and crossing the bridge together provides an exhilarating activity that each group's members will never forget.

The St. Ignace Antique Auto Show, held each June, has for many years provided a colorful bridge crossing that has featured old cars, hot cars, retro cars and classic cars. Where else can you merge the past with the modern present in such a perfect atmosphere as crossing the Mackinac Bridge?

Bicycle tours have enjoyed the crossing, as have parades of Harley Davidson motorcycles, Chevy Corvettes, motorcycle rallies and participants in the Richard Crane Memorial Truck Show, named for the founder of the American Truck Driving School in Coldwater, Mich.

The St. Ignace auto show weekend is responsible for the most traffic to ever cross the bridge in one day or one weekend – records that seem destined to stand until they are broken by the same event in a future year.

Bridge runners get their chance to run on Labor Day morning before the Bridge Walk begins. Participants must be selected in a special lottery conducted by each Michigan county well in advance of the event.

Vintage cars cross the bridge each year during the St. Ignace Antique Auto Show.

The retro parade of vehicles displays many models built long before the bridge was constructed.

A runner displays his exhilaration at nearing the finish line on the Big Mac.

Fudge Classic runners organized an event to cross the bridge together.

Runners in the Governor's Run/Walk event cross the bridge before the masses walk across on Labor Day.

The bicycle groups that cross normally do so at an early hour of the morning and are usually finished before many people realize they were on the bridge.

A support vehicle accompanies the riders, in case of difficulty crossing the span. A faltering rider or mechanical breakdown is simply loaded up and carried the rest of the way.

Most of the fare collectors get a kick out of seeing the parade vehicles come through and look forward to working the day or night of the event.

The Mackinac Bridge Authority is pleased to host the parade groups, and strives to allow the events to take place in a safe, organized atmosphere. A permit is necessary in advance to secure permission to cross the bridge in this manner.

A dramatic view from a bicyclists' perspective while crossing the Mighty Mac.

The bike tours usually are escorted across at 6 a.m.

A thundering line of nearly 1,200 Harley Davidson motorcycles crossed the Mackinac Bridge in a 2005 Harley owners group rally during their Great Lakes Tour.

The Mackinaw Motorcycle Rally is punctuated by a midnight ride across the bridge – a dramatic rush for those who participate in leathers while riding chrome mounts with spectacular paint and graphic art. It is by far the loudest parade held on the bridge, even louder than the truck show parade.

Two Harley Davidson lovers reminisce about their ride across.

The line-up of lighted, decorative trucks in the Richard Crane Memorial Truck Show draws crowds from downtown St. Ignace to the Mackinac Bridge approach to downtown Mackinaw City. The truck show is a most unusual sight, with around 100 trucks participating in the Mackinac Bridge Parade of Lights. The Michigan Department of Transportation gives annual permission for the trucks to display all their lights in the parade. The trucks are decorated with trim lights, underside lighting, black lighting, and moving images and murals that cast an eerie, other-worldly glow upon the bridge.

The Corvette Crossroads Parade adds a classy salute to its event by crossing the Mackinac Bridge. The Corvette Crossroads is held in Mackinaw City in August and draws plenty of attention with its evening crossing, held with usually cooperative warm weather and convertible tops down.

15

Fog in the Straits

The Straits of Mackinac can be a very foggy place, especially in the months of May and June, when rapidly warming air develops with the onset of summer and mixes with water that is still cold from a winter of being frozen solid.

Fog can develop during other seasons too, when the reverse effect is taking place in the fall and when water is trying to freeze in the winter. However, May and June are the months that produce the most fog and consequently the most incidents in the Straits surrounding the Mackinac Bridge.

June 25, 1958, the day before the bridge's gala dedication was to begin, two ships collided under the span in dense fog. No one was injured and damage to each vessel was slight.

The German motor vessel Korbeck collided with the S.S. New York News, the Cheboygan Daily Tribune reported.

Capt. Evor S. Kerr of the U.S. Coast Guard cutter Mackinaw was notified and prepared to head to the scene to give assistance. Help was also summoned from the Mackinac Island Lifeboat Station and the U.S. Coast Guard cutter Sundew.

Captains of both vessels called a short time later and told authorities that they were not in need of help and could both continue under their own power.

The ships then sailed on to their destinations.

Ice fog forms at water level as the Straits begin to freeze early in the winter.

On May 7, 1965, the limestone carrier Cedarville sank after a collision in a dense fog with the Norwegian vessel Topdalsfjord just east of the Mackinac Bridge. The Cedarville had a crew of 35, and 10 of them died in the accident.

The Cedarville carried 14,411 tons of limestone when it left its home port of Calcite, Mich., near Rogers City at 5:01 a.m. Captain Martin Joppich headed west towards the Straits of Mackinac in light fog at full speed, although there were reports of dense fog near the bridge.

Joppich established radio communications with an eastbound German ship, the Weissenberg, about three miles from the bridge. A port-to-port passing arrangement was made, but no confirming whistle signals were heard.

With visibility dropping below 1,000 feet, the lookout on the Cedarville reported fog signals coming from the relative direction of the Mackinac Bridge channel.

At 9:38 a.m., the Weissenberg passed under the Mackinac Bridge and radioed his progress to Joppich, who assumed that he was about to make visual contact with the German vessel.

But the Weissenberg's captain informed Joppich that his was not the closest ship to the Cedarville, that the vessel bearing down on him was a Norwegian freighter that had not been answering radio calls.

Joppich frantically tried to raise the mystery ship on the radio, but received no answer. He ordered a 20-degree turn to starboard and reduced his speed. The radar man reported the mystery vessel dead ahead.

The bow lookout shouted, "There she is!" and the Topdalsfjord loomed out of the fog just 100 feet away. Joppich ordered full speed ahead and a hard turn to starboard – and seeing the Cedarville's bow pass just ahead of the Norwegian ship's bow – then ordered a hard turn to port in a last desperate effort to swing the stern clear.

The Cedarville sank with the loss of 10 lives after a collision east of the Mackinac Bridge.

The Topdalsfjord sliced into the Cedarville, cutting a deep gash in the port side between the seventh and eighth hatch. At 10:10 a.m., when attempts to stop the flow of water with a collision tarpaulin failed, Joppich attempted to beach the Cedarville at Mackinaw City just two miles away. But the course the ship sailed was headed east, not south. Only 15 minutes later, the Cedarville rolled over to starboard and sank in 105 feet of water, 3.5 miles southeast of the bridge's center-span. The Cedarville had traveled 2.3 miles into deeper water instead of finding the beach to ground the vessel.

The Weissenberg picked up survivors and, with the help of the U.S. Coast Guard cutter Mackinaw, some of the casualties. The Mackinaw transferred all to the State Dock in Mackinaw City.

U.S. maritime law now provides for a local pilot onboard all foreign ships in the Great Lakes.

The collision caused significant bow damage to the Topdalsfjord, but the ship remained afloat.

The Greek freighter Castalia rammed into the bridge's north tower at 7 p.m. on June 9, 1968, in dense fog tearing out a chunk of concrete below the waterline 23 feet wide and 15 feet high. The incident stands as the most damaging to the bridge in the first 50 years of its history, although it didn't affect bridge operations or traffic on the span.

"Thousands of boats had gone under the bridge in those 11 years it had been open without even coming close," lamented Larry Rubin, the Bridge Authority's executive secretary from 1950-1984, "but this one managed to get 1,900 feet off course."

Damage is seen here above the waterline of the bridge's north tower after the Greek freighter Castalia slammed into it. Diver Dick Campbell is preparing to inspect the tower's underwater caisson, where more damage was apparent.

Rubin said the insurance company for the ship's pilot agreed to pay part of the cost, and the ship's owner negotiated to pay the rest.

The concrete was patched and tested, showing the tower to remain strong as a main support for the 42,000 miles of cable that hold up the bridge roadways.

"It cost $45,000 to repair the damaged section," Rubin said. "They spent more than a quarter of a million dollars to fix the ship."

The Castalia, built in Lubeck, Germany in 1953, suffered significant bow damage and took on water but was able to proceed to Chicago without assistance.

The Greek "salty" Castalia suffered significant bow damage after striking the bridge. The ship continued on to Chicago.

Three Marine Corps Reserve officers died on Sunday, Sept. 10, 1978 when their private plane crashed into one of 180 pairs of vertical 2-inch thick steel suspender cables hung from the main cable structure to hold up the bridge deck.

The point of impact was about 80 feet above the roadway and 120 feet south of the north tower. There was no damage to the bridge, which sheared off the wings of the single-engine Cessna 182 as it passed through 40-foot gaps between the suspender cables.

Pieces of the plane's wing and steering column were found on the bridge roadway, and other pieces of wreckage were spotted in the water on the west side of the span. A wheel believed to be from the plane was later recovered about five miles east of the bridge.

The victims were identified as Maj. Virgil Osborne, 35, and Capt. Wayne Wisbrock, 32, – both of St. Louis, Mo., – and Capt. James Robbins, 31, of

Fog can occur during all seasons of the year, and during unexpected weather. This photo was taken on March 2 of a late snowy winter.

Steel plates were lowered into place to repair damage to the bridge from the Castalia's impact.

Fog bells were used at the base of each tower to warn ships away from the caissons. Modern radar made them obsolete. The north tower bell is now on display at Bridge View Park.

Neosho, Mo. The officers, on active duty attached to the Marine Corps Reserve Station at Lambert Field in St. Louis, had spent the weekend on a "liaison visit" at Camp Grayling, where they were scheduled for a two-week training session in February, 1979.

Robbins owned the plane and was believed to have been the pilot. The three had planned to fly over Mackinac Island before returning to St. Louis and had taken off from the airport at Camp Grayling, a National Guard reserve camp in northern lower Michigan, less than half an hour before the crash.

Police theorized that the pilot may have been following I-75 from Grayling to Mackinaw City when he met thick fog, described as "pea-soup fog" by Larry Rubin. The plane was flying east to west when it clipped the third suspender cable south of the north tower on the east side of the bridge, soared about 60 feet across the span as pieces fell on cars crossing

Marine patrol boats gathered to search for the victims of a 1978 plane crash into the bridge's suspender cables.

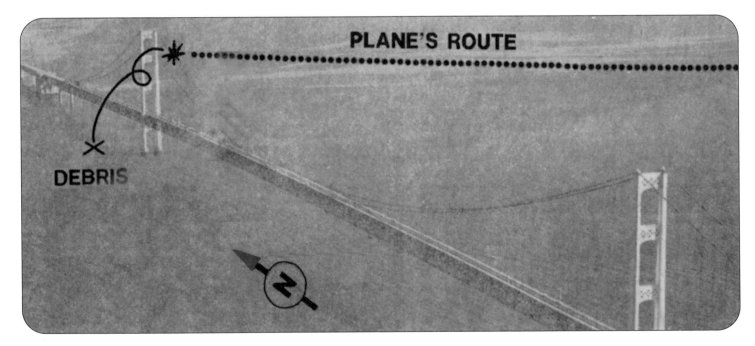

This United Press International newspaper graphic showed the likely route of a small plane that crashed through the bridge's suspender cables. Marks on the vertical cables later revealed that the impact was about 175 feet lower than shown in this depiction.

below on the roadway, then went between the first and second suspender cables south of the north tower and over the side, falling 250 feet into the water.

"The pieces of the plane that were found on the bridge had perfect imprints of that steel cable on them," Rubin said. "Green paint from the steel rope was embedded on a section of the wing. We also found a scrape, apparently caused by the plane's propeller, on one of the girders on the side of the bridge. It looked like it hit that as it tumbled over."

Police divers from the Michigan State Police and Mackinac County Sheriff's Department, assisted by Emmet County deputies and the U.S. Coast Guard,

recovered two of the bodies from beneath the bridge superstructure, but were unable to find the third man or the plane before darkness the day of the accident, hampered by underwater visibility of only three feet and swift currents.

The following day divers located the plane about 500 feet northwest of the bridge's north tower in 90 feet of water and tied a line to the fuselage. The wing piece and indentation indicated that the plane had struck the cable about six inches from the plane's fuselage. The third body was then recovered from inside the aircraft.

Plans to remove the wreckage from the water were abandoned when it appeared that it might break apart.

It may not be foggy in Mackinaw City or St. Ignace, but the Straits can often be another story entirely.

The bridge is usually obscured within the area of the suspension span when fog sets in, whether it is viewed looking to the north…

… or looking south along the causeway from St. Ignace towards Mackinaw City.

Fog can develop over the deep, cold waters of the Straits of Mackinac and obscure the Mackinac Bridge while the mainland shores experience clear visibility.

Supreme Sacrifices

With any worthwhile project or endeavor, there is a price to be paid and sacrifices to make. Usually these losses are measured in dollars and cents or in the amount of time spent. Rarely – other than in a situation involving war – would an entity be so bold as to predict the loss of human life associated with completion of an effort and still follow through with doing that business.

The construction industry has undergone many changes over the years, due in large part to OSHA regulations and the advent of modern safety equipment, engineering and architectural designs.

But in the early 1950s, at the time the Mackinac Bridge was being planned, estimates of one life being lost for every $10 million spent added up to 10 fatalities predicted to occur during construction. The amount of work being done at extreme depths, above very deep water and at exorbitant heights easily swelled the most conservative safety experts of the day to believe that a dozen men would be lost during the three years it would take to build the five-mile span.

In fact, the lives of five workmen were lost during the construction of the bridge between 1954 and 1957.

Another died during maintenance work in 1997.

Each a heartbreaking tragedy, the number was far below what was predicted by the "rule of thumb"

forecast by those in the industry, making the building and day-to-day work performed on the Mac quite safe in retrospect.

The beginning stages of the first construction season, 1954, did not start well when three lives were lost

Merritt-Chapman & Scott foremen stressed safety on the job.

in separate accidents during a 45-day period.

Hard-hat diver Frank Pepper became the first bridge fatality at the Straits on Sept. 10, 1954. An experienced diver with more than 20 years of underwater work, Pepper had been working for Merritt-Chapman & Scott at a depth of 140 to 150 feet for nearly an hour inspecting Pier 19, the bridge's south tower.

Divers of that era were dependent upon a tender who relayed hand signals from the diver tugging on a tether line to the crew topside that provided air and the means to lift the diver out of the water. The cumbersome, heavy gear worn in those days included a brass helmet, heavy suit with leather fittings and lead shoes. Unlike modern scuba divers utilizing lightweight equipment, early diving pioneers did very little swimming and instead exerted more effort simply moving about at depth in the hard-hat gear.

Tired and cold, Pepper signaled to his tender that he wanted to come up immediately.

Somehow in the process the diver was either raised too quickly or himself prompted too speedy an ascent, but upon surfacing was discovered to have contracted "the bends," or decompression sickness. Pepper was taken to a recompression chamber to attempt to dissolve the nitrogen bubbles that had formed in his bloodstream. He died before a doctor arrived.

Another Merritt-Chapman & Scott employee was lost exactly one month later on Oct. 10, 1954 when James R. LeSarge, 26, was killed in a fall inside the reinforced steel caisson foundation of Pier 20, the bridge's north tower. A welder, LeSarge fell through several steel braces and hit his head during a 40-foot drop to the bottom of the caisson which was being filled with concrete.

Stories often circulate about a worker that is buried in the Mackinac Bridge, but according to those who were on the job they are not true. It is believed that LeSarge died before reaching the bottom of the

foundation. His body was immediately recovered.

Only 15 days later a local worker from St. Ignace drowned, creating very low morale among the work crews. Albert B. Abbott slipped and fell into the Straits while walking on a beam that was 18 inches wide and only four feet above the water where he was working on a bridge foundation. He did not surface, causing his co-workers to jump in after him, but he was not immediately found.

He was dead by the time his body was recovered.

Hardhat divers were utilized during construction of the Mackinac Bridge, wearing brass helmets and lead shoes. They were tethered to surface support personnel and used air hoses connected to a topside compressor. Gordon Andrews (left) and Clint Passeno (top) assist Dick Campbell with his diving gear on a pier repair.

The next two workers died June 6, 1956 after falling from near the top of the north tower.

Jack C. Baker, a 28 year-old from Pagosa Springs, Col., and 27 year-old Robert Koppen of Plymouth, Mich., were working their first day on the job for the American Bridge Division when the accident occurred. The men were installing chain-link fence, or a spinners' platform, as an area where the cable spin-

ners could work while handling the thin wires that would be bulked together to comprise the main cables that support the bridge.

Bundles of the chain-link fence, folded up like road maps, were to be raised to the top of each tower. Five heavier wire ropes had been stretched from anchor block to anchor block, the complete 8,614-foot length of the total suspension. The bundles were tied

Workmen on the bridge had to watch their step from the beginning of their shift to the end. This Merritt-Chapman & Scott crew change shows the workmen boarding a tugboat for transport to the bridge site.

to the wire ropes with U-shaped brackets so they could slide down the wire ropes as they were unfolded. To hold the packages in place, a restraining line was tied to control their speed and the rate of descent down the supporting ropes.

There was no roadway below yet, only open air above the water as the construction crews worked to link the bridge towers and anchor piers with cable.

Robert Anderson, in charge of the detail, and his assistant Louis Stepman stood at the top of the tower to push each package with their feet to allow gravity to help the chain-link fence segments unfold.

Suddenly, the restraining line snapped. The 100-foot package of fencing and supporting 8-by-10-inch, 10-foot wooden ties slid out of control down the wire ropes and caught Baker and Koppen wrapped up inside, dooming them to plunge into the Straits from a height of more than 500 feet.

Stepman and Anderson fell when the bundle crashed but grabbed the fence and held on for their lives. Anderson broke his ankle but ended up on top of a section of fence when it stopped short of falling

The tower caissons were sunk in 210 feet of water and required frequent inspection by divers during construction.

Ironworkers did their jobs at dizzying heights above the Straits. Chain-link fencing is being stretched out to form a walkway near the suspension cables, yet to be spun.

into the water below. Stepman was hanging by his fingers to a vertical section just below Anderson that had broken away from the wire ropes.

The situation – still 400 feet above the water – seemed hopeless, and Stepman called above to Anderson that he intended to let go. Anderson told him to hang on and encouraged him to try to climb up the chain-link fence.

Stepman, a Native American, managed to untie his boots and kicked them off, and got a toe-hold in the fence. He then climbed up the vertical section, dangling in mid-air from the cable, and made it to where Anderson held on. Both were then rescued by other workers.

Baker's body did not sink and was soon recovered, but there was no sign of Koppen. Work on the bridge was suspended while a three-day search commenced with boats and divers, but Koppen was never found.

Bundles of fencing were being linked when two workmen fell to their deaths on June 6, 1956.

On the day the bridge was dedicated – June 28, 1958, the Michigan Building and Trades Council dedicated two bronze plaques, one engraved with the names of the five men who died during construction of the Mackinac Bridge and the other with the dignitaries responsible for financing and organizing the project. They were located on the west side of Pier 1.

On July 29, 1999 the plaques were re-dedicated and moved to the pillar closest to the entrance of the Colonial Michilimackinac Visitor's Center to be more visible to the public. Also corrected was the spelling of James LeSarge's name, originally misspelled.

The Mackinac Bridge claimed one of its own Aug. 7, 1997 when a bridge maintenance worker fell from a scaffold 70 feet into the Straits of Mackinac and drowned.

Daniel Doyle, 42, of Sault Ste. Marie was working with another painter on a 40-foot long swing platform or "pick," a motorized scaffold similar to those used by high-rise window washers. Doyle, a steeplejack, fell while painting within box beams on the underside of the bridge just north of the south anchor pier, known as Pier 17.

Eyewitnesses said it did not appear that heavy winds blew Doyle from the platform or that he had a heart attack before falling. Two other employees working with Doyle reported seeing him fall and hit the water feet first and briefly try to swim towards the shore before going under.

The Mackinac Bridge Authority's boat arrived within several minutes but could not find Doyle.

Sheriff's department dive teams from Mackinac County, Emmet County and Cheboygan County all responded along with the U.S. Coast Guard, but due

This plaque was dedicated in 1958 at the base of the bridge in Mackinaw City.

The box beams of the bridge's underside, where two workmen fell while painting in separate accidents.

to choppy seas and nightfall could not resume the recovery effort until the next morning. Doyle's body was recovered just before noon Aug. 8 in 95 feet of water, 30 feet away from where he was last seen, witnesses said.

A subsequent investigation ruled the death as accidental. A bridge spokesman said all the safety and motorized equipment assigned to the work crew was recovered, and that the equipment was intact and remained in sound operating condition.

The accident ended a stretch of more than 2.08 million hours of routine maintenance done on the bridge in 40 years without a fatality or serious injury.

For the 110 employees of the Mackinac Bridge Authority, the tragedy was like a death in the family. The close-knit group named the street between the maintenance garage and the Bridge Authority's offices "Daniel Doyle Drive" in memory of the worker. Doyle was a seasonal employee with the bridge's

Daniel Doyle Drive, named for a bridge maintenance worker killed on the job in 1997. The street runs between the Authority's Administration Building and the Maintenance Barn.

maintenance crew for 12 years.

The Doyle tragedy called to mind a similar circumstance from October, 1965, when a workman fell 115 feet from the bridge into the Straits but lived to tell about it. Emory McKelvie, 35, of Sault Ste. Marie, credited fellow workers that day with saving him from drowning in the chilly water, 90 feet deep where he went in.

McKelvie was painting from a swing stage, with ropes looped around each end, when a wind gust lifted one end and dumped him off. He dropped 40 feet and hit a cable beam two-feet high by two-feet wide, bounced off and plummeted another 80 feet into the water.

"He completely disappeared and must have gone down a long way, because I couldn't see him at all and you can usually see down in the water a ways when you're up that high," recalled co-worker Millard Jewell of Indian River. "I didn't think he would come up again after awhile."

Although weighted by his paint-soaked clothing, McKelvie surfaced at last and was obviously in trouble, but conscious. Jewell quickly climbed down a safety rope into the water and held McKelvic until a rescue boat reached the scene 1.5 miles from shore.

"He was hurting," Jewell said. "I think he had a broken arm and some broken ribs. I tied the rope around him and from there all I could do was wait. We felt pretty helpless in the water and I know they felt helpless up on the bridge, too. There was nothing anybody could do until that boat came out. We held on for more than a half-hour."

A crew foreman, James Petrone, of Pittsburgh, threw a life jacket down to the pair in the water.

"It was the right idea, but the wind and the current took it towards Lake Michigan and I made the mistake of going after it," Jewell said. "When I finally got to it I was exhausted and then the life jacket would barely float. It certainly wouldn't hold us both up. So I had to swim all the way back to 'Big Em,' as we called him, and hold us onto the rope. It was cold, I'll tell you."

Both men were hospitalized in St. Ignace for a couple of days and treated. They were employed by Universal Delta Co. of Bethlehem, Pa., painting contractors.

Today the Mackinac Bridge Authority has two boats and keeps one in the water on duty whenever maintenance workers are on the bridge, which are most days with reasonably calm weather between May and October. The boat now stands by in case it is needed to avert a tragedy like the one that happened with Doyle – and almost happened to McKelvie.

The Mackinac Bridge Authority's patrol boat, kept ready if needed to assist when maintenance workers are on the bridge. The boat patrols the waters onsite, near the workers.

The breath-taking view "down the slope," where two bridge workmen died in 1956 while installing a chain-link work platform for spinning cables.

This Merritt-Chapman & Scott change of crew was typical of the scenes at area docks, with workmen taking their lunch bags and a lot of determination on the job each day.

September 22, 1989

During the first 50 years of the Mackinac Bridge's history, one date stands out as the most public of all since it opened – a day that combined terror, tragedy, grief and controversy.

It is a date that many people will never, ever forget.

That date is Sept. 22, 1989 – when a light blue 1987 Yugo driven by Leslie Ann Pluhar of Royal Oak, Mich., went off the Mackinac Bridge.

A young woman's life ended in unimaginable horror, dying in perhaps the most spectacular way possible in Michigan, falling in a car from the state's most celebrated structure – its very symbol since 1957.

A family wrestled with incomprehensible pain for eight days until her body was recovered.

Claims that the bridge was unsafe resulted in a lawsuit, settled out of court five years later.

Mostly, the tragedy caused many in Michigan who had crossed the bridge at one time or another to ponder the sheer terror of the accident.

At 6:40 p.m. that Friday night, witnesses said the car careened out of control about 600 feet north of the bridge's south tower and struck the center median and straddled it for about 70 feet, then swerved back across two lanes and hit an 11-inch high curb rail almost head-on, flipping up along a

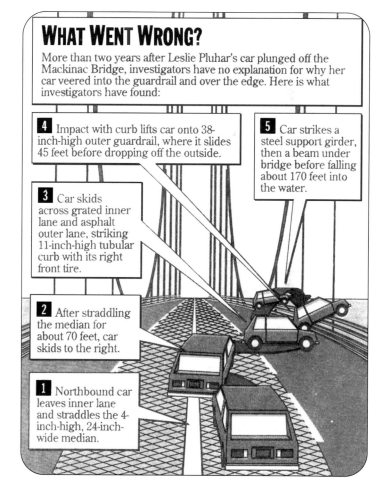

WHAT WENT WRONG?

More than two years after Leslie Pluhar's car plunged off the Mackinac Bridge, investigators have no explanation for why her car veered into the guardrail and over the edge. Here is what investigators have found:

4 Impact with curb lifts car onto 38-inch-high outer guardrail, where it slides 45 feet before dropping off the outside.

5 Car strikes a steel support girder, then a beam under bridge before falling about 170 feet into the water.

3 Car skids across grated inner lane and asphalt outer lane, striking 11-inch-high tubular curb with its right front tire.

2 After straddling the median for about 70 feet, car skids to the right.

1 Northbound car leaves inner lane and straddles the 4-inch-high, 24-inch-wide median.

The Detroit News summarized the accident in this 1991 illustration by graphic artist Moses Harris.

railing 3 feet 2 inches high and skidding for almost 40 feet, clipping off a streetlight pole before spinning sideways and hitting a vertical suspender cable. The cable impact, which nearly bisected the small car across the roof, apparently popped out the Yugo's rear window, which was found shattered but intact on a girder.

The car then fell – possibly upside down – onto a 21-inch girder that slopes down at a 45-degree slant for about 40 feet, where it meets a vertical and a horizontal girder. Paint was chipped on the angled girder most of the way down, maintenance worker Al Stempki told the Detroit Free Press.

Then the car plunged to the water, dropping free and clear for 180 feet and likely reaching 70 mph by impact.

"I think she had five, maybe six seconds before she hit the water," said Max Coburn, the Mackinac Bridge Authority's chief engineer, after studying the accident scene.

"The car was going at a high rate of speed and she hit the brakes on the steel grating lane, then let up on the brakes, hit the rail and bounced up, hit the other rail and kept on sliding, and rolled over the rail," Coburn theorized.

Trucker Donald Klassen of Manitoba was driving his rig on the outside lane, about five-car lengths behind the Yugo, which had just passed him. He didn't think Pluhar tried to stop.

"Even when she crossed the median, her brake lights did not come on," he told the Detroit Free Press.

Michigan State Police investigators estimated Pluhar's speed at 55-63 mph, a factor they said helped make the nearly head-on collision with the curb rail so deadly. Eyewitnesses contended that strong winds helped push the car off the bridge. But a wind gauge at center span, which would have recorded higher speeds than at the accident scene 600 feet north of the south tower, only clocked steady 35 mph winds during the hour before and after the accident with a max-

imum gust of 48 mph. Later that night, substantially windier conditions prevailed as the storm increased in intensity. The temperature at 7 p.m. on the evening of the tragedy was 43 degrees and the road deck was mostly dry, though rain fell in the area earlier.

Pluhar, 31, was traveling north to visit her boyfriend, 34 year-old Frederick Burton of Gould City, Mich., about 50 miles northwest of St. Ignace. While taking a six-month break from college after finishing at Oakland Community College, hoping to transfer credits to Wayne State University, Pluhar held part-time jobs at United Parcel Service and at the Clawson Steak House, where she waitressed.

Pluhar's driving record was cited by some as proof that the accident was likely caused by driver-error.

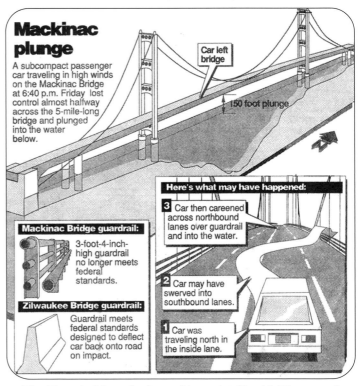

Mackinac plunge

A subcompact passenger car traveling in high winds on the Mackinac Bridge at 6:40 p.m. Friday lost control almost halfway across the 5-mile-long bridge and plunged into the water below.

Car left bridge

150 foot plunge

Here's what may have happened:

3 Car then careened across northbound lanes over guardrail and into the water.

2 Car may have swerved into southbound lanes.

1 Car was traveling north in the inside lane.

Mackinac Bridge guardrail:

3-foot-4-inch-high guardrail no longer meets federal standards.

Zilwaukee Bridge guardrail:

Guardrail meets federal standards designed to deflect car back onto road on impact.

The Detroit News had graphic artist David Pierce explore multiple topics related to the crash in this illustration days after the tragedy.

She had four speeding convictions, one drunken driving conviction, two license suspensions and one restriction between 1982 and 1984. She had no tickets since her license was reinstated in February, 1985.

The weather remained stormy for several days after the accident, and divers didn't get to begin searching for the car and driver until Sept. 27. They found their target the first day with a sonar unit towed behind a boat. The vehicle was upright in approximately 150 feet of water about 30 feet east of the Mackinac Bridge, along a slope that bordered a channel 300 feet deep.

Meanwhile, the Pluhar family arrived and remained sequestered in a St. Ignace motel, helplessly waiting for their daughter to be recovered. It seemed that media from every outlet in Detroit and perhaps the state of Michigan descended upon the Straits Area to cover the story. Many were tenacious in their efforts to find any bit of information the other guys didn't have in their many days of waiting for weather to break so the recovery could begin.

Police feared that currents would carry the vehicle down the slope and into waters too deep for recovery by divers. The crew

worked in six two-man dive teams, assembled from throughout the state. All wore special equipment much different from that used by sport divers, including full-face masks that facilitated two-way communication. The teams figured they had 18 minutes to work at depth before beginning their ascent, slowed by decompression stops to rid themselves of dangerous residual nitrogen that could cause "the bends"

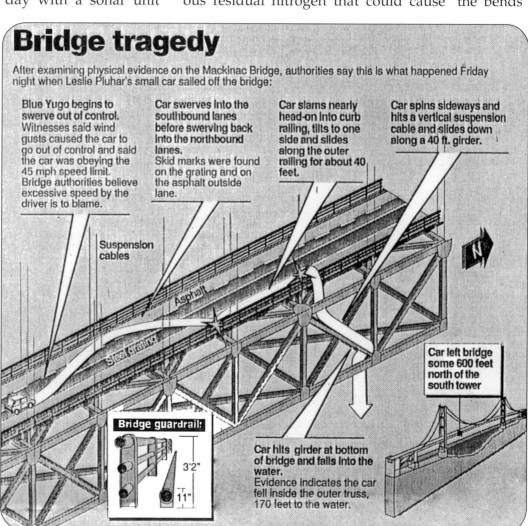

Bridge tragedy

After examining physical evidence on the Mackinac Bridge, authorities say this is what happened Friday night when Leslie Pluhar's small car sailed off the bridge:

Blue Yugo begins to swerve out of control. Witnesses said wind gusts caused the car to go out of control and said the car was obeying the 45 mph speed limit. Bridge authorities believe excessive speed by the driver is to blame.

Car swerves into the southbound lanes before swerving back into the northbound lanes. Skid marks were found on the grating and on the asphalt outside lane.

Car slams nearly head-on into curb railing, tilts to one side and slides along the outer railing for about 40 feet.

Car spins sideways and hits a vertical suspension cable and slides down along a 40 ft. girder.

Suspension cables

Asphalt

Steel grating

Bridge guardrail:

3'2"

11"

Car hits girder at bottom of bridge and falls into the water. Evidence indicates the car fell inside the outer truss, 170 feet to the water.

Car left bridge some 600 feet north of the south tower

N

David Pierce later depicted the path of Pluhar's Yugo as falling between the box-frame girders of the bridge in this Detroit News graphic.

resulting in death.

After first complaining to Michigan Gov. Jim Blanchard about the lack of progress in the recovery, the Pluhars sent word to the State Police Dive Team that their closure should not come at the expense of another life.

"They absolutely expressed their concern that no one get hurt in the recovery," said Lt. Michael Cushman, who headed the dive operation.

The first team down found the vehicle and veri-

Members of the Michigan State Police Dive Team prepare to descend 150 feet to the sunken Yugo. The divers battled weather, currents and icy depths to return Leslie Ann Pluhar's body to her family..

fied that the victim was inside, then left a float line tied to the car and the descent line tied to a 500-pound sinker normally used to anchor buoys. The idea was for each dive group to find the car in the darkness simply by following the line.

"When I first got there the line was about 15 feet short of the car, so I attached more line," said Michigan State Police diver Terry Fitzpatrick of Cheboygan, Mich. "At the time that 15 feet seemed forever, when you're not connected to anything. My first impressions of the scene were that I could not get over how badly damaged the car was. It clearly had struck the bridge several times on the way down, and the speed with which it fell to the surface must have been incredible."

Although the water temperature was 52 degrees at the surface, at 156 feet down it was 34 degrees, Fitzpatrick said.

"Because we had so little time to work I remember feeling very jumpy and keyed up," he recalled. "We had to rush to restrain the victim in the car, then loop the lift line around the wheels, through the axles and in the side windows and out the back. You feel tremendous pressure at that depth and probably some of it was the nitrogen narcosis from working so deep."

Fitzpatrick said he had never been down that deep before on any dive.

"It was a one-of-a-kind experience, believe me," he said. "It was the most

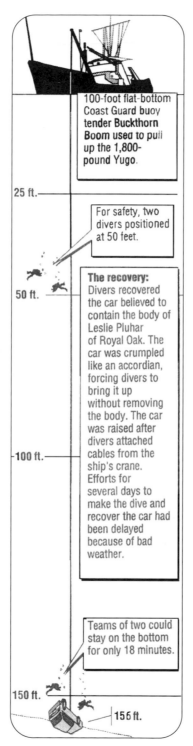

100-foot flat-bottom Coast Guard buoy tender **Buckthorn** Boom used to pull up the 1,800-pound Yugo.

25 ft.

For safety, two divers positioned at 50 feet.

50 ft.

The recovery: Divers recovered the car believed to contain the body of Leslie Pluhar of Royal Oak. The car was crumpled like an accordian, forcing divers to bring it up without removing the body. The car was raised after divers attached cables from the ship's crane. Efforts for several days to make the dive and recover the car had been delayed because of bad weather.

100 ft.

Teams of two could stay on the bottom for only 18 minutes.

150 ft.

156 ft.

complicated, hazardous job I've been on. I began to feel cold on the way up while hanging on the line for a decompression stop with another tank of air."

When the other dive teams completed the connections to prepare the lifting operation, the cable from the U.S. Coast Guard buoy tender Buckthorn still fell one foot short of the heavy line attached to the car. All divers had been to the bottom, using up their allotted time at depth. The operation was so close to succeeding – or failing.

"I had less residual nitrogen in me, so I went back with my partner to attach that line," Fitzpatrick said. "I felt much more relaxed on the second dive. With the wave action, the two ends would be too far apart, then real close. Finally they moved the boat a bit on the surface and we hooked it together."

One last bit of compassion for the victim occurred at that point.

"The woman's purse was up on the dashboard, and I was afraid it would fall out on the way up, so I reached in and I got it. I brought it up with me to the surface for her family. It was a team effort all the way when you consider all the groups that worked together out there."

The vehicle was brought to the surface under the bridge, slowly drained of much of the water inside, and raised to the deck of the Buckthorn. A tarpaulin was immediately thrown over the car.

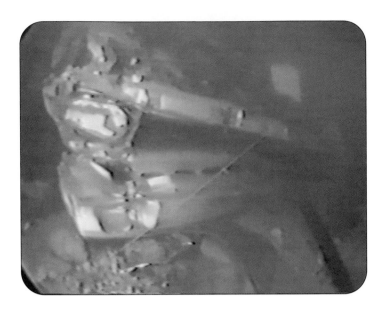

Underwater view of the Yugo on the bottom of the Straits.

The recovery was completed at 6:40 p.m. on Sept. 30, 1989 by the U.S. Coast Guard buoy-tender Buckthorn.

The wreckage barely resembled an automobile when it was placed on a flatbed trailer at the State Dock in Mackinaw City.

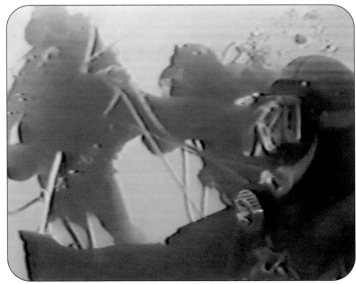

Michigan State Police divers spent long periods of time tethered to a safety line underwater to decompress after the car was raised.

Scores of spectators watched the recovery from the shores and from a half-dozen boats, using binoculars, telephoto lenses and 25-cent shore telescopes. A half-dozen members of Pluhar's family watched from a nearby cabin cruiser.

"Because of the extensive accordion-like damage to the front and rear of the vehicle, we were unable to extricate the victim first," Cushman told the Detroit Free Press.

The car was pulled to the surface at 6:40 p.m., almost eight days to the minute from the time it plunged from the bridge and disappeared.

The ship slowly motored to the State Dock in Mackinaw City, where the Yugo was uncovered and Pluhar's body removed. A waiting Mackinaw City ambulance transferred her to St. Ignace, where the coroner examined her and she was prepared for identification by her family. From there, she was taken to a Grand Rapids hospital for autopsy and released to her family for burial.

Leslie Ann Pluhar's long journey had ended, but in a touch of irony included a round-trip across the very bridge where she had lost her life.

The car was lifted by crane to a flatbed wrecker and taken to a Mackinaw City garage where it waited until State Police investigators were able to arrange transport for a complete investigation at their Lansing lab.

The story was far from over, proven by a $2 million dollar lawsuit filed by the Pluhar family that contended the bridge had inadequate warnings for bad weather, substandard guardrails, an insufficient dividing strip and dangerous gratings in the middle lanes of the suspended portion of the span.

A report done by a state Senate committee agreed, saying the bridge suffered from "fundamental safety flaws" and needed a higher median barrier, a higher curb and a different outer railing that curves inward.

But a report by a House committee called the bridge "the safest stretch of highway in Michigan."

Mackinac Bridge Authority officials maintained that the bridge was safe.

"Of some 80 million vehicles that have passed over this structure," Jim Ecker, the bridge's chief engineer, told the Detroit News in 1994, "one vehicle left the structure for reasons no one will really ever know. And the other 79,999,999 vehicles passed safely. That indicates a pretty good record."

An eyewitness surfaced for the plaintiff that stated he saw the car "blow off the bridge like a piece of paper," and the defense produced a State Trooper who said that Pluhar's foot was firmly against the gas pedal of the Yugo when first examined on the bottom of the Straits. A further statement maintained that the imprint of the gas pedal was visible in the sole of her right shoe.

Eventually, the New York engineering firm of Steinman, Boynton, Gronquist and Birdsall that built the bridge settled their share with the family for $50,000. Anthony Motors, the dealer that sold Pluhar the Yugo, paid the family the vehicle's cost of $5,000.

After reports that Aetna Insurance, representing the Mackinac Bridge Authority, and the Michigan Department of Transportation had offered the family $350,000 – with the family reportedly still asking for $800,000 – the two sides settled in Macomb County Circuit Court on Sept. 16, 1994, at $500,000 through the aid of a mediation panel of three lawyers. Any negotiations were hearsay, since the judge would have determined any damages.

Economics and risk had taken over the proceedings, and the lawsuit was dropped.

"The case is closed on Leslie Pluhar," said attorney Dennis Cotter, who represented the Authority.

The medical examiner's autopsy report listed drowning as the cause of her death.

18

The Unfortunate Choice

Unlike the Golden Gate Bridge, which crosses San Francisco Bay and allows pedestrian traffic from extremely populated areas, the Mackinac Bridge has had few incidents of suicide. The Golden Gate has unofficially totaled nearly 1,500 deaths as of 2007 while the Mackinac Bridge has recorded just a dozen.

No one who has ever jumped from the Mackinac Bridge has ever survived to tell about it. Several victims' bodies were never found after making the 175-200 foot leap - which takes about four seconds - into waters as much as 300 feet deep.

April 20, 1974 stands as a significant date in the bridge's history because until that Saturday night there had never been an occurrence like the one that confronted the driver of a bridge patrol vehicle crossing about 10:30 p.m. The patrol officer found a van parked near the middle of the span with no occupants. The vehicle's engine was running and a wallet inside belonged to the owner of the van, Russell James Weaver, 33, of Royal Oak, Mich.

A U.S. Coast Guard boat and plane searched the area the next day but turned up no trace of a body in the Straits, officials said. State police said they found no evidence of foul play. Weaver is believed to be the first person to take his own life from the Mackinac Bridge, but his body was never recovered.

On Sept. 5, 1985, 67 year-old Werner Paulick drove his car onto the bridge, stopped mid-span and got out and apparently jumped, although no one saw him do it. Paulick, a West German citizen living in Sterling Heights, Mich., was later found about one-mile west of the bridge in Lake Michigan.

The Mackinac Bridge Walk of Labor Day, 1987 provided the first real evidence of someone jumping from the bridge, because witnesses actually saw it happen.

Perfect weather greeted 51,500 walkers led by Michigan Gov. James Blanchard, and most had already completed the event when Ronald Robert Courier, 40, of Bay City, Mich., neared the north tower as one of the last pedestrians to cross that day. At 1:50 p.m. Courier removed his jacket, walked onto a beam and either fell or jumped 170 feet to the water below.

Eyewitnesses said it appeared at first as though the man was showing off, hanging out off the beam before letting go. The body, which was recovered about 4:50 p.m. by divers from the Mackinac County Sheriff's Department and the Mackinac Bridge Authority, had a significant blood-alcohol content level.

In that case, divers only had to submerge down an anchor line from the point of impact to find the body. Typically, the forces of gravity will take a body so deep that it may not resurface immediately.

But other conditions may prevent recovery, especially deep currents that can run counter to the wind direction on the surface. Experienced scuba divers who have visited shipwrecks in the Straits in varying conditions will tell you that conditions underwater are not always what they seem on the surface. There are days when divers submerge looking at a dive boat tied off in one direction from the wind, only to be surprised at depth when a compass reveals that the current is from a totally different direction.

Currents may have forever hidden the body of a woman believed to have jumped from just north of Pier 20, the bridge's north tower. On Sept. 11, 1987, Theresa Lu Burns, 28, of Indian River, Mich., abandoned her car late at night and was not found despite extensive searches of the area. Wind and water conditions changed frequently in the days, weeks and years that followed, but Burns' body was not recovered.

The same scenario played a role in the delayed recovery of Kimberly Ann Widmer, 25, of Cheboygan who abandoned her car on the Mackinac Bridge on Dec. 13, 1987. Her vehicle was found nearer to the Mackinaw City side, at Pier 11, just after 11 p.m., not as far out from shore as would be expected if she had jumped. Police found marks on the bridge railing that suggested she may have climbed over. A search of the area was unsuccessful, and strong northwest winds blew for days afterward, expanding the target area southeast towards the Mackinaw City shoreline. Further patrols and searches along the beach as far south as Point Nipigon and Bois Blanc Island produced nothing for nearly a week, and the search was called off. Her body was found eight days later on the beach at Good Hart, more than 36 miles to the southwest, a journey around Waugoshance Point that no one would have expected.

On Sept. 3, 1996 – a day after the Bridge Walk – a 62 year-old Novi, Mich., man jumped from the north anchor pier. Bich Ngoc Hoang, a Vietnamese native, stopped his Buick LeSabre in the northbound lane of the bridge near the north anchor pier before leaping into the Straits at 6:50 p.m. A crew from Coast Guard Station St. Ignace recovered the body shortly after

witnesses reported the jump. Officials said drowning and heart attack were the causes of death. Police said a note was found in the vehicle.

On April 22, 1998 witnesses said a man stopped his northbound vehicle in the right lane about 40 feet north of the south tower, got out and jumped over the railing about 2:50 p.m. Barry Michael Ducher, 37, of Southfield, Mich., was rescued quickly by Bridge Authority workers replacing grating on the bridge and the Authority's workboat, assisting with repair work at Pier 2. The U.S. Coast Guard helped remove the man from the water, and he was taken to Mackinac Straits Hospital in St. Ignace. The hospital announced that he had died about two hours later. The site where Ducher had fallen, 170 feet below the bridge superstructure, is very close to where the Yugo crashed off the span nine years before.

The afternoon of Oct. 5, 2001 marked the occasion of the third known female to jump from the bridge. Pamela Faulkner, 39, from Trout Lake, Mich., parked her vehicle on the southbound side of the north anchor pier at 4:45 p.m. and climbed onto the pier wall, and then jumped, witnesses reported. The Coast

U.S. Coast Guardsmen recovered the body of a Vietnamese man who jumped from the bridge in 1996.

Guard was dispatched to assist with the woman's recovery from the water. A medical examiner pronounced her dead a short time later.

On Aug. 15, 2002, an unusual mystery presented itself to authorities when Mackinac Bridge personnel were alerted to a white 1992 4-door Honda Civic abandoned at mid span around 2 a.m. An investigation by responding Michigan State Police from the St. Ignace Post indicated that Mindy Arnett, 20, and her six month-old daughter, Jersey, were missing and may possibly have fallen or jumped over the side of the bridge into the Straits below. The young mother and daughter were from Stockbridge, Mich., northeast of Jackson.

A U.S. Coast Guard HH-65 helicopter from Air Station Traverse City conducted three searches of the area over a 14-hour period that resulted in no sightings that day. Simultaneously, the Coast Guard Cutter Katmai Bay, and multiple small boats from Coast Guard Station St. Ignace, Mackinac County Sheriff's Department and the Sault Tribal Police continued searching.

Searchers used surface vessels, planes, helicopters, and two sophisticated side-scan sonar devices, one from the MSP and a second from the Great Lakes Shipwreck Historical Society of Sault Ste. Marie, in their search patterns but were unsuccessful. The high-tech equipment allowed searchers to cover an area 10 times larger and much more thoroughly than with divers. Bad weather and high winds initially hampered the search team. The University of Michigan offered assistance by providing a computer model of where the bodies might be located taking into account currents, winds, and weight of the missing persons with no results.

While searching, the team did find a new shipwreck in 120 feet of water – the William Young – a schooner that had not been seen in more than 110 years.

According to Lt. Pat London of the MSP, the comprehensive efforts showed nothing in terms of recovering either of the purported victims.

"This was the largest search ever conducted in the Straits area," London said. "Making the decision to suspend the operation was difficult. "The indications are they did go in the water. With that in mind, everyone on the search team is very disappointed that we have not located these individuals. Our hope was to recover the bodies and provide the family with some degree of closure to this tragedy."

Had the young woman jumped with her child, or was she perhaps picked up by a passing vehicle? Did she have a reason to disappear?

An investigation showed that Mindy Arnett had taken her infant daughter the day before she went missing from a relative's home where she had been placed by a judge.

Her purse was still inside the car. Police found a palm print on the bridge railing, but no sign of Mindy or her baby.

The relative – Lisa Oaks of Flint – had been raising her little sister's baby, Jersey, since she was 2 1/2 months old. She had temporary custody because the 20-year-old had experienced a variety of emotional problems. But Mindy seemed to be turning her life around.

Two weeks prior to the disappearance, Mindy was allowed her first unsupervised visits with Jersey. On Aug. 14, Oaks left them alone, and they disappeared.

She reported them missing, then received word that Mindy's car was found on the Mackinac Bridge. Oaks' sister and niece had vanished.

"Since the incident, we have had no credible leads to suggest that the woman or the baby are alive," Michigan State Police Lt. Curt Robertson said in 2007. "The investigation looked into the possibility that a second vehicle had picked them up. You can speculate, but there is no proof as they've never been found anywhere."

Robertson said that the names of Arnett and her daughter have been placed into the nationwide lien system and authorities would be alerted in the event that the pair was found alive somewhere.

Likewise, records are on file for comparison if remains are eventually discovered.

"The case is not closed, but it is inactive pending further evidence," Robertson said. "We review it every six months but there's been nothing new for a long time."

Early on the morning of Feb. 5, 2007, a car was found abandoned on the northbound side of the bridge, between the north tower and the north anchor pier. Ice covered the Straits below the spot where the car was found, but a hole in the ice and other evidence led police to believe that Gary Morris, 57, of Sault Ste. Marie had leapt to his death.

Besides being the first recorded instance of this type during the winter months where someone had jumped, it also marked the first time the bridge's video camera system saw what had happened.

"Before the camera system was installed, there were other incidents where we found a car abandoned on the bridge and never found a person who may have gone over," Mackinac Bridge Authority Administrator Robert Sweeney said. "Some of those instances went unreported long ago, back in the 1960s, because the connection just wasn't made. Now we can see what happens on the bridge."

On March 2, 1997, a leased 1996 dark green Ford Bronco crossed the bridge heading southbound. At mid-span, 25 year-old Richard Alan Daraban passed a slow-moving tractor-trailer and suddenly swerved hard to the right, skidded along the bridge rail and pitched over the side, falling 200 feet into the Straits of Mackinac.

Witnesses stated that Daraban was traveling at a high rate of speed, estimated by Michigan State Police who measured "yaw marks" from the vehicle's tires on the bridge railing at 60-65 mph.

"That indicated that the Bronco was sliding sideways on the railing at that point," said Lt. Myles McCormack, commander of the St. Ignace Post, "for a distance of about 120 feet."

Police added that there was no evidence that Daraban tried to stop the car, and one witness said the act appeared to be deliberate.

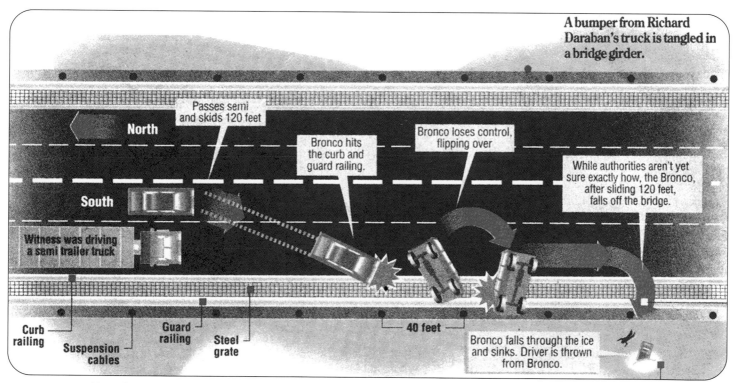

Detroit Free Press graphic artist Rick Nease portrayed the flight of Richard Daraban's Bronco in 1997.

Richard Daraban's 1996 Bronco was recovered from water nearly 200 feet deep under the bridge on March 5, 1997, three days after he crashed over the rail at mid-span.

"It appears that the death was the result of a deliberate act on his part and not the result of a flaw in the Mackinac Bridge," State Police Col. Michael Robinson said on March 24.

An attorney for Daraban's family said that family members do not accept suicide as an explanation for Richard Daraban's death, and maintained that faulty-designed low railings on the bridge were to blame.

Daraban's body was found on the ice below the bridge, but his vehicle broke through two feet of ice and sank to the bottom. His body was recovered within hours by a U.S. Coast Guard helicopter crew.

A police investigation portrayed Daraban as a troubled young man with a history of drunken driving convictions and other moving violations, and said that he was under considerable family and job stress in the days before he headed north from his suburban Detroit-area home. His drive time to the bridge was just enough to cross once and head back south, police said.

The Michigan Secretary of State's office said that his driver's license was suspended 10 times and was never renewed after it lapsed nearly five years earlier.

An autopsy showed no evidence of alcohol or drugs in the victim's body.

In an effort to avoid endangering divers in recovering the Bronco from a depth of nearly 200 feet and extremely cold water, a remote-controlled submersible vehicle was used to survey the wreck with a video camera before its remote arm attached a chain to the truck. The bottom drops off to a depth of nearly 300 feet in that area.

The U.S. Coast Guard cutter Biscayne Bay and the

Mackinac Bridge maintenance workers and local law enforcement agencies have had several occasions where they have talked people out of jumping off the bridge. At times, incidents have produced copy-cat attempts. Families sometimes call the Bridge Authority offices to report that a relative is on their way north to jump.

Canadian Coast Guard cutter Griffon teamed to raise the Bronco, which rested on its side along a slope after currents had swept it 30-40 yards east of the bridge. The M-Rover was loaned from the University of Michigan's Department of Naval Architecture and Marine Engineering.

The Bronco was recovered the afternoon of March 5.

Not all the troubled souls who become so despondent as to want to use the bridge to end their lives wind up having the nerve to do it.

A 46 year-old Genesee County man was talked off the railing of the bridge on July 14, 1993 by the commander of the Michigan State Police Post at St. Ignace. A passing prison bus official reported a pedestrian on the bridge at 2:30 p.m. that day. Lt. Newton Jerome, post commander, answered the call and found a man sitting on the rail of pier 17, his vehicle parked nearby. The man said he had made a special trip up north from his Flint-area home to get to the Mackinac Bridge.

Jerome talked the man out of his intention and took the man into custody for a trip to Northern Michigan Hospital in Petoskey for evaluation.

The date of April 26, 1995 proved to be another good example of intervention when a 29 year-old Kawkawlin man initiated a three-hour stand-off at Pier 17. The man, upset over family problems, parked his car at the bridge's south anchor pier around 1 p.m. and was reported by a passing motorist 15 minutes later. The report stated that there was a man drinking a beer on the edge of the pier wall. When approached by maintenance workers and police, the man threatened to end his life and hopped onto the 24 1/4-inch diameter suspension cable and began walking up towards the south tower with a six-pack of 16-ounce beers.

Bridge workers Mark Kinjorski and Glen Lewis accompanied him on the cable, giving him a jacket and gloves to ward off the steady winds. A report in the St. Ignace News stated that the workers' reminders of Mother's Day coming soon and the man's four year-old son elicited only stoicism. He was also impervious to pleas from Michigan State Police

troopers, St. Ignace and Mackinaw City police, and a minister brought in from a nearby church. Bridge official Calvin McPhee offered to give the man a Mackinac Bridge Authority hat if he climbed off the cable, prompting a smile but little else.

Police considered subduing the muscular man, but St. Ignace Police Sgt. Fred Paquin said that idea was considered too risky for all involved.

After demanding a cell-phone, the man did make contact with several individuals and climbed another 100 feet higher to escape traffic noise from the roadway, juggling the beer and the cell-phone.

At 4:17 p.m. the man climbed down to awaiting officers and was transported to a local hospital for examination. The Bay County Sheriff's Department, which had a warrant for commitment of the man, sent deputies to take him to a mental institution near Bay City.

State Trooper Roger Gady, who first responded to the complaint, wound up staying behind because another possible jumper was reportedly approaching the bridge. Police had received word that a 43 year-old Central Lake, Mich., woman was distraught and driving to the bridge with plans to jump off. Using subject and vehicle descriptions, Gady spotted the woman and pulled her over as she drove onto the span. She was taken into protective custody and police learned there was an outstanding mental health commitment order for the woman out of Antrim County.

That day, everyone had a happy ending.

"I always thought that there might have been people who came up here with the idea of ending their lives, but then changed their minds when they saw how beautiful it was up on the bridge," speculated Larry Rubin in 2006. "I think the populations of our area and San Francisco and the pedestrians allowed on the Golden Gate are the big differences."

Although unintentional, an unfortunate choice made by a Lansing, Mich., man led to his death July 7, 1988 after a midnight walk onto the bridge.

Scott Alan Ulman, 20, and four other young

Lansing-area residents were on their way to Pier 17 when they were spotted by a bridge patrol officer. Upon seeing the patrol car stop, all five subjects ran – some climbing over the rail and hiding under the bridge within the box beams. Soon, all but Ulman were accounted for.

A search of the area under and around the bridge proved unsuccessful, and State Police conducted an air and water search over the days that followed. Ulman's body was found July 12 on Wawatam Beach, just west of the Mackinac Bridge on the Lake Michigan side.

The Mackinac Bridge does not allow pedestrian traffic and has had minimal incidents of suicide. No one who has ever jumped has survived to tell about it. The drop from mid-span is estimated to last about four seconds with speeds of approximately 80 mph.

19

Bridge Safety Today

How safe is it to cross the Mackinac Bridge today? Security has increased on the bridge in recent years, preparing since Sept. 11, 2001 for exactly the type of possibility that emerged Aug. 12, 2006 when three Texas men were arrested in Caro, Mich., and charged with collecting material to support terrorist acts and surveillance of a vulnerable target with intent to commit terrorism.

The men were arrested after buying nearly a thousand pre-paid cell phones favored by terrorist organizations at a Wal-Mart. Caro's police chief said cell phones can be used as detonators, and prosecutors in a similar case in Ohio have said prepaid cell phones often are used by terrorists because they are not traceable.

The bridge is kept open in all types of weather by its dedicated maintenance crew.

The crew plows snow and sands the bridge deck to help with traction. It can all be pushed into the lake – where it came from in the first place – or scooped up in the spring.

Investigators found photos of the Mackinac Bridge on the suspects' digital camera, and concluded they were going to blow up the bridge on Labor Day.

The trio's van was found to contain a laptop computer with information that authorities say led them to believe that "the Mackinac Bridge is the target at issue."

The FBI would later say the men were not terrorists and were not targeting the Mighty Mac. The U.S. Coast Guard increased patrols at the bridge pending the results of the investigation.

Patrols of the five-mile span have increased since a new Michigan State Police Post opened just steps away from the tollbooth plaza at the north end of the bridge.

A project to completely sandblast and re-paint the entire bridge resulted in several moveable work platforms being installed under the bridge's road deck around 2000. Workmen can move from one spot to another under the suspended portion of the bridge on the motorized platforms, which travel along a set of I-beam rails affording a view of the superstructure's underside.

More recently, video cameras have been installed throughout the entire length of the bridge, viewable on computer screens in the Mackinac Bridge Authority's offices in St. Ignace.

Bridge administrators and State Police spokesmen won't say what additional measures may be in place due to possible terrorist threats.

On August 21, 2006 the Mackinac Bridge Authority released a security statement about safety on the bridge. It read:

"Although specifics cannot be discussed, the general public should rest assured that the Mackinac Bridge Authority (MBA) has a very comprehensive security plan in place," said MBA Administrator Bob Sweeney. "The MBA coordinates its security plan and

A motorized platform now in place under the bridge's suspended span allows workmen to move freely in a north-south direction for maintenance tasks.

Bridge workers have a good view of the bridge's underside from the motorized work platform.

procedures in collaboration with the Michigan State Police and the U.S. Coast Guard. Since Sept. 11, 2001, the MBA has dramatically increased security at the bridge and developed a very detailed plan for the Annual Bridge Walk. Assistance is provided from 13 law enforcement agencies during this high-profile event. We believe our security procedures ensure the highest level of safety and provides a pleasurable experience for all participants (and travelers) that will cross the Mackinac Bridge during this event."

Since the 1989 accident that saw Leslie Pluhar's Yugo plunge from the bridge, electric message signs have been installed at both approaches to the span capable of warning motorists of current conditions at the Straits including wind speeds, road conditions and fog. Strobe lights were placed at the 45 mph posted speed limit signs just before the water's edge, making them more visible. Radio broadcasts on two different frequencies are available to be picked up on car radios with safety information.

In addition, a new policy was implemented to caution high profile vehicles – mostly campers and trucks – when wind speeds reach 20 mph. They previously were warned when wind speeds reached 25 mph.

Bridge employees escort such vehicles when winds reach 30 mph. Under the previous policy, drivers of these vehicles were given escorts when winds reached 35 mph.

A distant view of the Straits on a windy day can belie actual conditions on the road deck of the bridge. Safety procedures now in place close the Big Mac or restrict traffic flow for short periods until conditions abate.

In 1999 the Mackinac Bridge was selected the state's No. 1 Civil Engineering Project of the 20th Century by the Michigan Section of the American Society of Civil Engineers (ASCE).

"Crossing over to the U.P. on the Mackinac Bridge has become second nature to us, and it is easy to forget the planning and design that went into constructing this amazing structure," Michigan Lt. Gov. Posthumus said at a press conference Dec. 14, 1999.

Coming in second and third were the Soo Locks and the Detroit Windsor Tunnel. The Ambassador Bridge ranked fourth.

"The top projects were chosen because they made significant economic and social contributions to the state in its success as an industrial leader in the world by opening up channels of international commerce, protecting the environment, and improving the efficiency and safety of transportation," said Don Mercer, P.E., ASCE Michigan Section President.

Sponsors of the event included AUC, Michigan's Heavy Construction Association; the American Consulting Engineers Council; Associated General Contractors; Consumers Energy Company; the Michigan Asphalt Paving Association; Michigan CAT; the Michigan Concrete Association; the Michigan Concrete Paving Association; the Michigan Road Builders Association; and the Michigan Society of Professional Engineers.

Founded in 1852, ASCE represents more than 120,000 civil engineers worldwide, and is America's oldest national engineering society. There are 2,350 members in Michigan.

On Jan. 15, 2002 the American Road and Transportation Builders Association (ARTBA) selected the Mackinac Bridge and the Edsel Ford Freeway as Michigan's top two infrastructure projects of the 20th century.

To celebrate ARTBA's 100th anniversary that year, the group selected two projects in each state as construction, design, and engineering marvels.

In recent years critics of the bridge's design and safety systems took note of several incidents where the rails and curbs performed as specified.

An elderly couple nearly made history as being the third car to go over the side of the Mackinac Bridge, but were saved by the same railings criticized

Wind direction and speed is closely monitored along with other weather data from various locations in the Straits and at center-span on the bridge.

The bridge's operations center has instant contact with law enforcement agencies on both sides of the bridge, throughout Michigan and beyond.

in the other two incidents.

On a March afternoon in 1997, the couple traveled northbound in the right-hand lane when their Buick was hit by another car, Michigan State Police told the Cheboygan Daily Tribune.

A 35 year-old Holland, Mich., man driving a Chevrolet Camaro was reportedly weaving in and out of traffic behind the Buick and struck it from behind, sending the vehicle over the lower guard rail and striking a higher one, according to Trooper Mike Johnson of the St. Ignace Post.

"That guard rail did its job perfectly and kept the car from going over," Johnson said.

The driver of the Camaro continued on to the toll-booths and was asked to hand over his identification by Mackinac Bridge Authority officials who had heard a report about the accident from another driver.

The man sped away and continued on I-75 to the St. Ignace exit and drove into town, where he was apprehended by State Police.

He was arrested for drunken driving – third offense, driving with a suspended license and fleeing the scene of an accident. The man was taken to the Mackinac County Jail.

The elderly couple suffered only minor injuries, police said.

An average of 12,000 vehicles cross the Mackinac Bridge per day, with full traffic loads of 60,000 vehicles estimated during holiday periods. Ship traffic under the bridge is responsible for millions of tons of iron ore annually freighted to steel mills along with other cargoes to various ports.

Nearly 40,000 vehicles have crossed the bridge in one 24-hour period - during a weekend of the St. Ignace Antique Auto Show - the one-day record.

Cameras now make the entire length of the bridge visible and recordable in the Authority's offices.

Violent storms can strike at the Straits, but bridge personnel constantly monitor conditions to ensure safety.

Dr. David B. Steinman designed the Mackinac Bridge in such a way that this could not happen.

Tacoma Narrows Bridge Disaster

This photograph shows the twisting motion of the center span just prior to failure on Nov. 7, 1940.

A few minutes after the first piece of concrete fell, this 600 foot section broke out of the suspension span, turning upside down as it crashed in Puget Sound. Note how the floor assembly and the solid girders have been twisted and warped. The square object in mid air (near the center of the photograph) is a 25 foot section of concrete pavement. Notice the car in the top right corner.

The nature and severity of the torsional movement is revealed in this picture taken from the Tacoma end of the suspension span. When the twisting motion was at the maximum, elevation of the sidewalk at the right was 28 feet higher than the sidewalk at the left.

This photograph shows the sag in the east span after the failure. With the center span gone there was nothing to counter balance the weight of the side spans. The sag was 45 feet. Also illustrated is the immense size of the anchorages.

This photograph actually caught the first failure shortly before 11 a.m., as the first concrete dropped out of the roadway. Also note bulges in the stiffening girder near the far tower and also in the immediate foreground.

This picture was taken shortly after the failure. Note the nature of the twists in the dangling remainder of the south stiffening girder and the tangled remains of the north stiffening girder.

20

Comparing Big Mac

Few are as big as the bridge at the Straits of Mackinac.

The Mackinac Bridge is currently the third longest suspension bridge in the world.

Suspension bridges are measured by the length of the total area that is suspended.

In 1998, the Akashi-Kaikyo Bridge in Japan became the longest with a total suspension of 12,826 feet. The Great Belt Bridge in Halsskov-Sprogoe, Denmark, which also opened in 1998, is the second longest suspension bridge in the world with a total suspension of 8,921 feet.

The Mackinac Bridge is still the longest suspension bridge in the western hemisphere. The total length of the Mackinac Bridge is 26,372 feet. The length of the suspension bridge (including anchorages) is 8,614 feet. The length from cable bent pier to cable bent pier is 7,400 feet. The length of the main span (between towers) is 3,800 feet.

The Akashi-Kaikyo Bridge, also known as the Pearl Bridge, is a suspension bridge in Japan that crosses the Akashi Strait; it links Maiko in Kobe and Iwaya on Awaji Island as part of the Honshu-Shikoku Highway. As of 2007, it ranked as the longest suspension bridge in the world, substantially longer than the

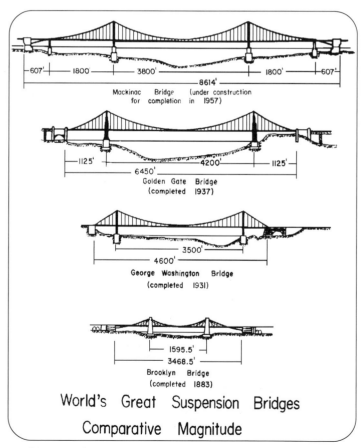

This 1956 diagram compared the four greatest bridges to date. Two have been built since that are longer than the Big Mac.

second-longest suspension bridge, the Danish Great Belt Bridge. It was planned to be one of three Honshu-Shikoku connecting bridges, annexing two borders of the Inland Sea.

Before the Akashi-Kaikyo Bridge was built, ferries carried passengers back and forth across the Akashi Strait in Japan. This dangerous waterway often experiences severe storms, and in 1955, two ferries sank in the strait during a storm, killing 168 children. The ensuing shock and public outrage convinced the Japanese government to draw up plans for a suspension bridge to cross the strait.

Actual construction did not begin until May 1988 and the bridge was opened for traffic on April 5, 1998.

The Japanese bridge has three spans and allows for six lanes of traffic. The central span is 6,531 feet, with the two other sections each at 3,150 ft. The bridge's total suspension is 12,831 feet long overall. The central span was originally only 6,528 feet but was stretched by more than three feet in the Kobe earthquake of January 17, 1995. It was designed on a two-hinged stiffening girder system, allowing it to withstand 178 mph winds, earthquakes measuring up to 8.5 on the Richter scale, and harsh sea currents. The bridge also contains pendula which operate at the resonant frequency of the bridge to dampen forces on it. The two main supporting towers are 978 feet above sea level, and the center span has a clearance of 213 feet above the water.

The Akashi-Kaikyo Bridge can expand up to six feet in one day.

The total cost is estimated at $5 billion. This cost is expected to be defrayed by charging commuters a toll to cross the bridge. However, the $20 toll is so high that very few drivers actually use the expensive bridge, preferring instead to use the slower-but-cheaper ferries.

Akashi Kaikyo Bridge in Japan - longest in the world.

The Mackinac Bridge is the third-longest suspension bridge in the world, and the longest in the Western Hemisphere.

The Great Belt Fixed Link is the series of connections between the Danish islands of Zealand and Funen across the Great Belt. It consists of a road suspension bridge and railway tunnel between Zealand and the island of Sprogø, as well as a box girder bridge between Sprogø and Funen. The "Great Belt Bridge" commonly refers to the suspension bridge, although it may also be used to mean the girder bridge or the link in its entirety. The suspension bridge, known as the Eastern Bridge, has the world's second-longest free span.

The link replaces the ferries which had been the primary means of crossing Great Belt for more than 100 years. After decades of speculation and debate, the decision to construct the link was made in 1986; while it was originally intended to complete the railway link three years before opening the road connection, the link was opened to rail traffic in 1997 and road traffic in 1998. At an estimated cost of $3.6 billion, the link is the largest construction project in Danish history.

Great Belt Bridge – second-longest in the world.

In order to pay back the construction expenses, the road connection is a toll road, and train operators pay a fixed toll per train in order to cross. The link has reduced travel times significantly; previously taking about an hour by ferry, Great Belt can now be crossed in about 10 minutes. The one-way toll for a motor vehicle is approximately $25.

In order to connect Halsskov on Zealand with Knudshoved on Funen, 12 miles to its west, a two-track railway and a four-lane motorway had to be built, aligned via the small islet Sprogø in the middle of the Great Belt. In general terms, the project comprised three different construction tasks: The Eastern Bridge for road transport, the Eastern Tunnel for rail transport and the Western Bridge for road and rail transport combined.

Built between 1991 and 1998, the Eastern Bridge is a road suspension bridge between Halsskov and Sprogø. It is 22,277 feet long with a suspended span of 8,921 feet, making it the world's second-longest suspension bridge. The vertical clearance for ships is 213 feet. At 833 feet above sea level, the two towers of the Eastern Bridge are the highest points on solid structures in Denmark. Only some radio masts are taller.

To keep the main cables tensioned, an anchorage structure on each side of the span is placed below the road deck. Additionally, a total of 19 concrete pillars (12 on the Zealand side, seven by Sprogø), each separated by a distance of 633 feet, carry the road deck outside the span.

The Strait of Messina Bridge was a planned suspension bridge that was to cross the Strait of Messina, a narrow section of water between the eastern tip of Sicily and the southern tip of mainland Italy. After years of discussion and planning that had come very close to beginning construction, the project was cancelled by the Italian government in October 2006.

Construction was to begin in 2006 and was expected to be completed in 2012. If completed, it would have been the largest suspension bridge in the world.

The 2006 plan called for a single-span suspension bridge with a central span of about two miles. This would have made the span more than 60 percent longer than the Akashi-Kaikyo Bridge in Japan.

Plans called for six traffic lanes (two driving lanes and one emergency lane in each direction), two railway tracks and two pedestrian lanes. The towers would have been anchored in more than 400 feet of water, with the suspended portions above water 2,000 feet deep.

Completion was planned to take 11 years, at a projected cost of more than $5 billion.

On October 12, 2006, the Italian Parliament voted 272 to 232 in favor of scrapping the plan due to the bridge's "doubtful usefulness and viability," as well as the inability of the already burdened Italian treasury to bear its share of the cost. Additionally, the road and rail links leading to the location of the proposed bridge were questionable as to their capabilities of supporting enough traffic to make the bridge profitable.

Other reasons for stopping the plan were earthquake risk and fears that much of the costs would be diverted to organized crime bosses, who could obtain a monopoly on construction contracts by intimidating competitors and bribing local officials and then overcharging for the work, generating large profits.

Many also questioned the priority of the bridge, since some towns in Sicily are still without running water, and claim that the money used for the bridge would be better spent elsewhere. The funds reserved for building the bridge will instead be used to improve ferry service between Messina (Sicily) and the mainland at Villa San Giovanni in Calabria and hydrofoil service from Messina to Reggio di Calabria, as well as other transportation projects.

The Strait of Messina Bridge as proposed by engineers. The towers would have been anchored in 400 feet of water and the center-span would have been over water that is 2,000 feet deep.

The Strait of Messina, located between Italy and the island of Sicily.

Michigan's Mackinac Bridge blends serenely with its peaceful surroundings on a quiet summer evening, still the greatest American bridge and the country's longest suspension-span bridge.

A winter sunrise frames the Mackinac Bridge amidst ice floes in the Straits of Mackinac.

If You Seek a Pleasant Peninsula…

On Oct. 31, 2006, the Mackinac Bridge Authority and the Michigan Department of Transportation announced the release of the official 50th Anniversary logo commemorating the opening of the Mackinac Bridge. The bridge celebrated 50 years of service in 2007 after first opening to traffic on Nov. 1, 1957.

"We think it appropriate to celebrate this milestone in the history of our majestic structure, which has become a national icon and well-known Michigan

Winter sunshine illuminates the bridge on a bright afternoon.

landmark," said Barbara J. Brown, MBA Board member and chair of the 50th Anniversary Committee.

The MBA Board also approved special celebrations for July and November 2007, focused on the 50-year milestone along with plans for parades, honorary ceremonies, demonstrations by iron workers, live history presentations, photo displays, musical entertainment, fireworks, release of a commemorative medallion, and other Straits Area community events.

Indeed Michigan's greatest symbol deserved plenty of fanfare and honors. The bridge that Dr. David B. Steinman at first said would last 1,000 years – then amended his statement to say that he had miscalculated, "the Mackinac Bridge will still be standing after the pyramids of Egypt have fallen," had weathered its first 50

© 2006
Mackinac Bridge 50-Year Celebration logo. Used with permission.

years in glorious fashion.

Expertly maintained, fully funded and amazingly resilient to the many forces and factors of man and nature that had failed to seriously affect its status as the lone highway link between Michigan's two main peninsulas, the Big Mac has endured plenty.

The structure is ready for more – lots more.

The bridge is perhaps the most photographed feature among the state's icons and has as many faces and moods as there are angles of sun, moon and weather. People drive from long distances to see it and enjoy the clean water-washed air of the Straits Area and its beaches, forests and attractions.

This can be done from either side of the Straits.

The Mackinac Bridge Authority hosted a grand opening of its new eight-acre Bridge View Park on June 12, 2002.

"The site of the new park has been a popular place for people to visit and enjoy the bridge," said Henry A. Lotoszinski, executive secretary of the Mackinac Bridge Authority in 2002. "These improvements will provide a beautiful setting for the public to experience the spectacular view of the span along with the Straits Area."

The observation building has five window sections facing the Straits of Mackinac and two entry doors. The back portion of the building has two restrooms and a small office area.

The bridge viewing area has been a popular place for people to visit and enjoy the Mackinac Bridge. The

A calm evening provides a mirror-like image of the Mackinac Bridge and its lighting pattern.

park provides a beautiful setting for the public to experience the spectacular view of the Mackinac Bridge and the Straits Area.

"The construction of this wonderful park has long been a dream of the Mackinac Bridge Authority," said Authority Chairman Murray D. Wikol. "The newly landscaped park will enhance the gateway to Michigan's Upper Peninsula."

Construction of the $1.3 million Bridge View Park began in April, 2001 and is located west of the toll plaza in Moran Township. The new park includes paved access roads, a walking path, picnic areas, trees and landscaped areas containing flowers and shrubs. The observation building is open from 8 a.m. until 9 p.m. daily.

The Authority also announced that another Mackinac Bridge token was placed in circulation, displaying the same front as the first gold token, except for the updated year. The back of the token has a "Bridge View Park" theme.

On the Mackinaw City side, public parks line the shores near the Old Mackinac Point Lighthouse, giving access to the water and a fabulous view of the bridge from the south. Seasonal restroom facilities are available with sidewalks, drinking fountains and pic-nic areas.

Truly, the Straits of Mackinac epitomizes the state motto of Michigan, "Si quaeris peninsulam amoenam, circumspice," or "If you seek a pleasant peninsula, look about you."

Bridge View Park under construction in 2001.

2007 will be remembered as a year of celebration for the Mackinac Bridge.

Views of the Mackinac Bridge from the Mackinaw City shoreline parks are some of the most photogenic locations and perfect for family outings.

A winter sunset colors the Straits with a purple hue.

Bridge View Park is now the home of one of the original fog bells used at the base of the towers in pre-radar days.

A view looking north, towards St. Ignace, from atop the south tower of the bridge.

A view from the top of the north tower, looking south towards Mackinaw City, on a bright sunny day.

The Mackinac Bridge Authority seeks to assist its customers in safely crossing the span.

In 2003, the following fares were established for those crossing the Mackinac Bridge:

Passenger Vehicle   **$1.25 per axle**
Passenger car, van, motorcycle, station wagon, SUV, pick-up truck, and school bus. (A van is a two-axle four tire vehicle not primarily intended for carrying cargo or commercial goods.)

Motor Homes   **$2.00 per axle**
A motor vehicle constructed or altered to provide living quarters, including permanently installed cooking and sleeping facilities, and is used for recreation, camping, or other non-commercial use.

All Others   **$3.00 per axle**
Vehicles not meeting passenger vehicle or motor home characteristics including but not limited to tractor trailers, buses, and step or cube vans. All vehicles will be classified by the lead vehicle. Anything being towed will be charged the per axle rate of the lead vehicle.

Commuter Cards and Tokens
You can purchase a commuter card with 24 passes or a roll of 24 tokens for $36 ($1.50 per crossing) and save 40 percent off the standard passenger vehicle fare. Commuter tokens can be purchased at the tollbooths. Commuter cards and tokens can be purchased at the customer services window in the Mackinac Bridge Authority Administration Building. The tollbooths accept cash only. The service window accepts cash and checks only. Towing trailers or other vehicles is not allowed with cards or tokens.

Transport Services
The Mackinac Bridge Authority provides transport services for pedestrians, bicyclists and snowmobilers who are not allowed to cross on their own. Fees are:

Passengers	$2.00
Bicycles	$2.00
Snowmobile and driver	$10.00
(Extra passenger)	$2.00

IMPORTANT DATES

- Mackinac Bridge Authority Appointed ....June, 1950
- Board of Three Engineers Retained........June, 1950
- Report of Board of Engineers..............January, 1951
- Financing and Construction Authorized by Legislature ....April 30, 1952
- D.B. Steinman Selected as Engineer...January, 1953
- Preliminary Plans and Estimates Completed ....March, 1953
- Construction Contracts Negotiated .....March, 1953
- Bids Received for Sale of Bonds...............................December 17, 1953
- Began Construction ....May 7, 1954
- Open to traffic.............................November 1, 1957
- Formal dedication...........................June 25-28, 1958
- 50 millionth crossing.................September 25, 1984
- 40th Anniversary Celebration ....November 1, 1997
- 100 millionth crossing ....June 25, 1998

The Straits of Mackinac freezes solid in the winter, but the bridge was built to withstand 2 1/2 times all the stresses of nature recorded in the area.

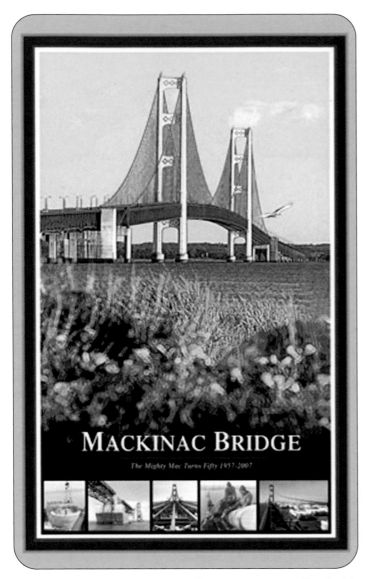

The Michigan Department of Transportation offered this poster as one of a series commemorating the bridge's 50th Anniversary.

Mackinaw City residents who feared in 1957 that the bridge and I-75 would bypass the little village would be amazed at the economic surge the transportation link has provided to the community.

The serenity of a Straits summer evening is captured in the Mackinac Bridge's graceful lights.

The Mackinac Bridge is a simple design but holds a great complexity in the numbers involved in designing, building and maintaining it. For your consideration:

CONCRETE

Total Concrete in Bridge
466,300 Cu. Yds. • 356,512 Cu. Meters

Total Concrete in Substructure
451,000 Cu. Yds. • 344,814 Cu. Meters

Total Concrete in One Anchorage
(No. 22)
91,600 Cu. Yds. • 70,033 Cu. Meters

Total Concrete in One Pier (No. 19)
80,600 Cu. Yds. • 61,623 Cu. Meters

Total Concrete in Superstructure
15,300 Cu. Yds.. • 11,698 Cu. Meters

CABLES

Total Length of Wire in Main Cables
42,000 Miles • 67,592 km

Maximum Tension in Each Cable
16,000 Tons • 14,515,995 kg

Number of Wires in Each Cable
12,580

Weight of Cables
11,840 Tons • 10,741,067 kg

Diameter of Main Cables
24 1/4 Inches • 62.23 cm

Diameter of Each Wire
0.196 Inches • .498 cm

LENGTHS

Total Length of Bridge (5 Miles)
26,372 Ft. • 8,038 Meters

Total Length of Steel Superstructure
19,243 Ft. • 5,865 Meters

Length of Suspension Bridge
(including Anchorages)
8,614 Ft. • 2,626 Meters

Total Length of North Approach
7,129 Ft. • 2,173 Meters

Length of Main Span
(between Main Towers)
3,800 Ft. • 1,158 Meters

DESIGN AND DETAIL DRAWINGS

Total Number of Engineering Drawings
4,000

Total Number of Blueprints
85,000

WEIGHTS

Total Weight of Bridge
1,024,500 Tons • 929,410,766 kg

Total Weight of Concrete
931,000 Tons • 844,589 kg

Total Weight of Substructure
919,100 Tons • 833,793,495 kg

Total Weight of Two Anchorages
360,380 Tons • 326,931,237 kg

Total Weight of Two Main Piers
318,000 Tons • 288,484,747 kg

Total Weight of Superstructure
104,400 Tons • 94,710,087 kg

Total Weight of Structural Steel
71,300 Tons • 64,682,272 kg

Weight of Steel in Each Main Tower
6,500 Tons • 5,896,701 kg

Total Weight of Cable Wire
11,840 Tons • 10,741,067 kg

Total Weight of Concrete Roadway
6,660 Tons • 6,041,850 kg

Total Weight of Reinforcing Steel
3,700 Tons • 3,356,584 kg

RIVETS AND BOLTS

Total Number of Steel Rivets
4,851,700

Total Number of Steel Bolts
1,016,600

MEN EMPLOYED

Total, at the Bridge Site.....................2,500
At Quarries, Shops, Mills, etc. 7,500
Total Number of Engineers 350

HEIGHTS AND DEPTHS

Height of Main Towers above Water
552 Ft. • 168.25 Meters

Maximum Depth to Rock at Mid-span
Unknown • Unknown

Maximum Depth of Water at Mid-span
295 Ft. • 90 Meters

Maximum Depth of Tower Piers below Water
210 Ft. • 64 Meters

Height of Roadway above Water at Mid-span
199 Ft. • 61 Meters

Under-clearance at Mid-span for Ships
155 Ft. • 47 Meters

Maximum Depth of Water at Piers
142 Ft. • 43 Meters

Maximum Depth of Piers Sunk through Overburden
105 Ft. • 32 Meters

MICHIGAN'S MIRACLE BRIDGE

In humility and reverence
we dedicate this work of faith.
And with pride we behold what
vision, courage and determination
have wrought.

A poem in steel.
A dream-span on bed-rock.
A symphony in metal and stone.
The mystical union of beauty and
strength.
A lyric pattern etched
against the blue.
God working through man to confute
the powers of evil and to add another
stanza to the hymn of creation.

This is the Song of the Bridge:
With hammer-clang on steel and rock.
I sing the song of men who build.
With strength defying storm
and shock,
I sing a hymn of dreams fulfilled.
I lift my span, I fling it wide,
And stand where wind and
wave contend.
I bear the load so men may ride
Whither they will, and to what end.
The light gleams on my
strands and bars
In glory when the sun goes down.
I spread a net to hold the stars
And wear the sunset as my crown.

With humble pride and wonder, we
look up to gaze upon the Bridge.
Outsoaring gravity and space, it
rises from the waves on shining
strands to arch across the sky
in lofty grace.
Seen from above, a battleship
appears dwarfed like a toy beneath
the vaulting span.
This is our triumph over ancient fears.
A Bridge of Peace,
wrought of the dreams of man!

Before it was built,
we envisioned the Bridge.
We saw it clearly and
clairvoyant bright:
Twin sky-piercing towers
of majestic rise.
The power-packed cables in
symmetry of parabolic arcs.
The titan uplift of the singing strands.
The lofty roadway bearing multitudes
high above the waves.
And deep beneath the waves and
tides, the massive caissons founded
upon bed-rock, enduring as
the pyramids.

by D. B. STEINMAN,
Consulting Engineer

There is timeless strength in those
towers and poetry in the cable-borne
span. The two are
harmoniously joined.
Between the two pierced steel
towers, framing the azure of the
sky, the arching roadway slowly
sweeps upward to meet the swift
downward sweep of the cables.
These curves and proportions
were not accidents.

It is no accident that the Mackinac
Bridge is a thrill to the beholder,
to lift the heart with pride and
the soul with thankful prayer.
It was planned that way.
A lifetime of dedicated purpose,
long years of consecrated effort,
the highest yearnings of the human
soul, went into the planning and
building of this masterwork.

85,000 Blueprints.
A million tons of concrete and steel.
Twenty-million man-hours of
sweat and toil and courage
and sacrifice.
But, above all these, the
priceless ingredient—
the Spirit of Consecration.
And that includes the qualities
of vision, devotion, inspiration
and integrity.

That is why the Mackinac Bridge
will endure.
That is why the Mackinac Bridge
is majestic.
And that is why the Mackinac Bridge
is beautiful.

In the planning and building of
Michigan's Miracle Bridge, no effort
was spared, nothing was stinted.
The highest attainments of the
science and art of bridgebuilding
went into the design.
The best qualities of materials and
workmanship went into the
construction.
The finest qualities of honor and
loyalty and teamwork went into
the consummation of this
great project.

These are eternal verities:
There is no excellence without effort.
There is no achievement
without vision.
There is no consummation
without faith.

The Mackinac Bridge is a triumph of
science and art.
But, more than that,
the Mackinac Bridge is a monument
—an enduring monument to vision,
faith, and courage.
Without the vision, faith, and courage
of the people of Michigan—
their leaders, their statesmen,
their workers—this great Bridge
could never have been built.

This is the heroic saga
of the Mackinac Bridge:
Generations dreamed the crossing;
Doubters shook their heads in scorn.
Brave men vowed that
they would build it—
From their faith the Bridge was born.
There it spans the miles of water,
Speeding millions on their way—
Bridge of vision, hope, and courage,
Portal to a brighter day.

—D. B. Steinman

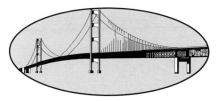

Acknowledgements

Writing a book about a bridge may sound like a boring topic to some.

If you only look at a bridge as a mass of steel and concrete that allows passage from one place to the next, there's not much excitement.

Now, consider the story of a bridge that combined an entire state; that became a form of architectural poetry and inspired artists and photographers for half a century.

From the day it opened there have always been many great stories about the Mackinac Bridge that needed to be told.

In the Mighty Mac's first 50 years, there have been many crossings, events and historic moments that begged to be assembled for the public to read. There were funny publicity stunts in the early years and plenty of wild weather that the bridge has endured. There are people who have been afraid to cross it and those who have had accidents. A stalwart crew of workmen still keeps it in tip-top shape and hundreds of hands have reached out to take the tolls paid to cross it.

All have stories to tell.

Gathering the funny, the sad, the tragic and the unusual would have been a much more laborious task without the help of Susan Godzik and the resources of the wonderful Michigan Room at the Mackinaw Area Public Library. Mackinaw City is indeed fortunate to have such a wealth of information about the Mackinac Bridge, the Straits Area, and the state of Michigan in one annex.

To the library and staff, I am deeply indebted.

The bridge's most public moments have been told by leading newspapers of the state, and my grateful thanks go to the Detroit News, Detroit Free Press, Grand Rapids Press, Lansing State Journal, Sault Evening News, St. Ignace News, Petoskey News/Review and fellow staffers and co-workers at my own Cheboygan Daily Tribune for their assistance, courtesies and access to archived information.

This book became a reality through the patience of composition editor Dan Pavwoski and graphic artists Charles Borowicz and Renee Glass. They expanded my horizons and challenged my creativity to give the concept a higher dimension.

The Mackinac Bridge Authority's present-day staff, especially Bob Sweeney, Dean Steiner and Lorraine Garries is thanked for their willingness to help chase down dates and recall memories and circumstances. Past administrator Walter North took a special interest in helping me organize people, places and topics in the bridge's history.

In addition, many local law enforcement personnel helped in significant ways.

When it came to getting the facts right, I was lucky to have a resource nearby like Dick Campbell, who worked on the bridge as a diver, painter, maintenance man and so much more during his years of employment there. He opened his home to me and welcomed my questions. Dick wanted this book to be a legacy to those who maintained the Mac, and I couldn't have agreed more.

The Michigan Department of Transportation is deserving of special thanks for its generosity in accessing archival photographs from a meticulously organized and maintained database.

Finally, there could have been no greater motivating factor than Larry Rubin, who already wrote two books about the bridge at Mackinac. One was about the construction process and the other about the political process of putting together people, funding and opportunity to build a magnificent structure to link Michigan's great peninsulas.

No attempt here is made to rewrite these works or improve on their content. My subject matter is merely a continuance of those well-written volumes, and only seeks to serve the record with a 50-year update of what has happened on; over and under this great bridge and feature the accounts of those who were there with pictures that helped to tell the story.

It is my hope that those who read this work will better appreciate all that went into past crossings, and further marvel at David B. Steinman's genius during their next trip across.

Photo Credits

The author gratefully acknowledges the work of Herm Ellis, Mickey Duggan and Harold Bell, photographers for the Mackinac Bridge Authority. Their timeless work captures an era when the bridge was being built and in its infancy. The assistance of the Michigan Department of Transportation's Photo Section is appreciated for its generous cooperation in contributing to this book. Many personal collections are also acknowledged below, in addition to the work attributed to newspapers.

About The Author

Mike Fornes

Mike Fornes has covered the Mackinac Bridge for more than 20 years for several media outlets in Northern Michigan, including radio and television stations and the Cheboygan Daily Tribune.

He broke the story of Leslie Pluhar's Yugo plummeting off the bridge for WPBN/WTOM TV 7&4 after noticing police lights on the span from the dining room window of his home on the Straits. The incident was named the top news story in the state of Michigan for 1989.

A resident of Mackinaw City, Mich., he enjoys scuba diving and sailing among his interests in the Straits of Mackinac area.

Fornes is frequently in demand as a guest speaker and presenter to tour groups, cruise ship organizations and historical societies. He estimates that he has given more than 1,500 tours of the Mackinac Bridge from motorcoaches, cruise boats and shore-based presentations.

He is also the author of "USCGC Mackinaw WAGB 83 – An Illustrated History of a Great Lakes Queen" published in 2005.

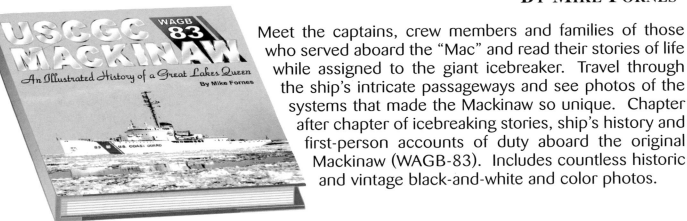

POINTS OF VIEW

Why Are Some People
HOMELESS?

By Emma Jones

Published in 2018 by
KidHaven Publishing, an Imprint of Greenhaven Publishing, LLC
353 3rd Avenue
Suite 255
New York, NY 10010

Designer: Seth Hughes
Editor: Katie Kawa

Photo credits: Cover Bob Rowan/Corbis Documentary/Getty Images; p. 5 (top) Arman Zhenikeyev/ Shutterstock.com; p. 5 (bottom) asiseeit/E+/Getty Images; p. 7 Nieuwland Photography/ Shutterstock.com; p. 9 John Moore/Getty Images; p. 11 Konstantin L/Shutterstock.com; p. 13 mikeledray/Shutterstock.com; p. 15 Fresnel/Shutterstock.com; p. 17 Monkey Business Images/ Shutterstock.com; p. 19 © istockphoto.com/KatarzynaBialasiewicz; p. 21 (chalkboard) Rawpixel/ iStock/Thinkstock; p. 21 (photo frame) FARBAI/iStock/Thinkstock; p. 21 (inset, left) Spencer Platt/ Getty Images; p. 21 (inset, middle) SAUL LOEB/AFP/Getty Images; p. 21 (inset, right) Feverpitched/ iStock/Thinkstock.

Cataloging-in-Publication Data

Names: Jones, Emma.
Title: Why are some people homeless? / Emma Jones.
Description: New York : KidHaven Publishing, 2018. | Series: Points of view | Includes index.
Identifiers: ISBN 9781534523364 (pbk.) | 9781534523388 (library bound) | ISBN 9781534523371 (6 pack) | ISBN 9781534523395 (ebook)
Subjects: LCSH: Homelessness–Juvenile literature. | Homelessness–United States–Juvenile literature.
Classification: LCC HV4493.J66 2018 | DDC 362.5'92–dc23

Printed in the United States of America

CPSIA compliance information: Batch #BS17KL: For further information contact Greenhaven Publishing LLC, New York, New York at 1-844-317-7404.

Please visit our website, www.greenhavenpublishing.com. For a free color catalog of all our high-quality books, call toll free 1-844-317-7404 or fax 1-844-317-7405.

CONTENTS

More Than
ONE ANSWER

Homelessness is a sad fact of life for millions of Americans, including families and children. They live in **shelters**, in cars, and sometimes on city streets because they don't have a home of their own.

Why are some people homeless? There isn't one answer to that question. Helping the homeless starts with understanding the many different reasons why people end up without a home. Some people may think certain reasons are more important to address than others, depending on their point of view. It's important to have all the facts when trying to talk about such a tough **topic**.

Know the Facts!

Around 3 million people live without a home for some amount of time each year in the United States.

It's good to know as much as possible to have an informed, or educated, opinion about homelessness in your community.

5

Harmful
POINTS OF VIEW

People who are homeless have often faced hard times in their lives that forced them into a shelter or onto the streets. However, some people still have an uninformed point of view about why people are homeless. They believe most homeless people live that way because of their own poor choices.

Some people see those who are homeless as **criminals** or other dangerous, or unsafe, people to be around. This point of view is harmful because it sometimes leads to attacks on homeless people. Homeless people are still people, and all people should be treated with understanding.

Know the Facts!

As of 2015, more than 1 million homeless people had some kind of job.

Some people think those who are homeless should just get jobs. It's not that easy, though. Many homeless people do have jobs but still can't afford a place to live.

Money
PROBLEMS

Many people who already live in **poverty** are one unlucky event away from losing their home. One of the leading causes of homelessness is not having enough income, or money from work, to afford a home. Income is lost when someone loses their job or dies.

Sometimes, though, people still have a job but lose their home. They need the money they use to pay for their home for something unexpected. This can include **medical** bills, a new car, or a **divorce**.

Know the Facts!

More than 37 percent of the homeless population is made up of families.

Families who lose their homes because of low income or unexpected expenses often don't stay homeless for long.

No Place
TO GO

Another major cause of homelessness is a lack of affordable housing. In recent years, the cost of rent has been rising in the United States. At the same time, the number of affordable housing **units** has fallen. This is a dangerous combination that leads to homelessness.

When people can't make payments on their home, something called foreclosure can happen. This is when a person loses the right to their home because they can't make the payments on it. In the last 10 years, foreclosures have played a big part in people becoming homeless.

Know the Facts!

In 2010, the United States reached the peak of what's sometimes called a foreclosure crisis. This happened when banks improperly foreclosed on a large number of homes across the country.

10

The government has been spending less money on low-income housing. This has made it harder for people to afford a place to live.

Mental Illness and

HOMELESSNESS

In some cases, homelessness is caused by more than just financial problems. Health problems can lead to someone becoming homeless. This is certainly true for people who suffer from **mental** illnesses.

Mental illnesses often cause people to become unable to take care of themselves and their home. They also cause people to push away those who might help keep them from becoming homeless. People who are in danger of becoming homeless often don't have access to good mental health care. Leaders of major U.S. cities have said better mental health services are needed to fight homelessness.

Know the Facts!

It was reported in January 2016 that one in five people who were homeless suffered from a **serious** mental illness.

Veterans, or people who served in the military, often suffer from **physical** and mental problems when they return from war. This has led to a large homeless veteran population in the United States.

Drug
ABUSE

Some people believe all homeless people **abuse** drugs or alcohol. Although this isn't true, substance abuse, such as drug and alcohol abuse, is a leading cause of homelessness, especially for single adults.

Substance abuse costs money, which could be used to pay for housing. It can also cause people to lose their job and push away loved ones, which could lead to homelessness. In some cases, people begin abusing drugs and alcohol after they become homeless. They believe it can help them forget their problems for a while. However, it only makes those problems worse.

14

Know the Facts!

Substance abuse and mental illness often are seen together in homeless populations. People use alcohol and drugs to deal with their mental illnesses instead of getting proper care.

Abusing drugs and alcohol can cause many problems in a person's life, including homelessness.

VIOLENCE

For some people, their home is no longer a safe place to be. They choose to become homeless because it might actually save their lives. About 12 percent of the homeless population in the United States is made up of survivors of domestic **violence**, which is violence and abuse that happens in the home.

Women suffer from domestic violence more often than men. These women often have little financial freedom. This makes it hard to find a place to live if they choose to leave their abuser. They sometimes have nowhere else to go but shelters.

Know the Facts!

One in three women and one in four men have suffered from domestic violence at some point in their life.

Homeless shelters can provide safe places for people who've suffered from domestic violence. They can stay there until they find housing away from their abuser.

17

Not Just
ADULTS

Adults aren't the only people who can become homeless. Children and young adults become homeless for many reasons. In some cases, they run away from home and have nowhere else to go. In other cases, their family kicks them out of the house.

A large number of homeless young people were part of the foster care system, in which a young person is cared for by someone other than their parent for a period of time. When young people become too old for the foster care system, they sometimes find themselves without a place to live.

Know the Facts!

About 1 in 30 children in the United States was homeless for some period of time in 2014, which was when the last major study of American homelessness was done.

It's hard to know exactly how many young people are homeless because they don't want to say they're living without a home and often act as if they're not homeless.

19

How Can
YOU HELP?

Why are some people homeless? There isn't one answer to that question. Many things—from the loss of a job to problems in a family—can cause someone to become homeless. Understanding all these reasons helps people form educated points of view about homelessness and how to help those who live without a home.

You can help the homeless in your community by **volunteering** at a shelter or soup kitchen. You can also give food, clothing, and blankets to places that help people who are homeless. How else can you help?

Know the Facts!

Between 2015 and 2016, the homeless population in the United States went down by 3 percent.

Why are some people homeless?

- emergency that uses up income
- mental illness
- loss of income
- parents kick children out
- aging out of foster care system
- domestic violence
- drug or alcohol abuse
- lack of affordable housing
- problems for veterans who come back from war
- children run away from home
- foreclosure

These are just some of the many reasons people are homeless in the United States. What do you think should be done to fix these problems?

FORECLOSURE

FOR SALE

21

GLOSSARY

abuse: To misuse or mistreat. Also, misuse or mistreatment of someone or something.

criminal: A person who is guilty of a crime.

divorce: The act of legally ending a marriage.

medical: Relating to the practice of treating something wrong with the body.

mental: Relating to the mind.

physical: Relating to the body.

poverty: The state of being poor.

serious: Having dangerous possible outcomes.

shelter: A location that provides food and a place to stay to those who need it.

topic: A subject.

unit: A single thing that is part of a whole, larger thing.

violence: The use of force to harm someone.

volunteer: To do something to help because you want to do it.

For More INFORMATION

WEBSITES

The National Coalition for the Homeless

www.nationalhomeless.org

This group is made up of people who want to end the problem of homelessness, and its website includes information on different ways people can work toward this goal.

Snapshot of Homelessness

www.endhomelessness.org/pages/snapshot_of_homelessness

The National Alliance to End Homelessness presents a basic look at facts and figures about homelessness in the United States.

Zoom Into Action: You Can Help People Who Are Hungry or Homeless!

pbskids.org/zoom/activities/action/way02.html

This website shows many ways young people can help the homeless in their community.

BOOKS

Ancona, George. *Can We Help?: Kids Volunteering to Help Their Communities.* Somerville, MA: Candlewick Press, 2015.

Lüsted, Marcia Amidon. *I Am Homeless, Now What?* New York, NY: Rosen Publishing, 2017.

INDEX